Basic Health

Charles LaRue

AGS®

American Guidance Service, Inc.
Circle Pines, Minnesota 55014-1796

THE AUTHOR

Charles J. La Rue holds a Ph.D. in science education, zoology, and botany from the University of Maryland, and an M.A. in zoology and botany from the University of Texas. Dr. La Rue has been involved in the teaching of health topics in his fourteen years as a biology teacher. He has spent two years as a zoology and botany instructor at the college level, and seventeen years as a supervisor of elementary science in the Montgomery County (Maryland) Public Schools. He has been responsible for curriculum development and implementation in nutrition and the use of alcohol, drugs, and tobacco. He is the author of *Basic Biology. The Science of Living Things*. He participated in the early development of BSCS Green Version of *Biological Science: An Ecological Approach*. He has coauthored fifty-five learning packages in science. He has also coauthored with Paul Brandewein *100 Investigations in Laboratory Science*. He serves as a consultant for the National Geographic Society for educational filmstrips, films, and books.

CONSULTANT

Elissa D. Weinroth, Ph.D., served as consultant, contributor, and preliminary editor for the text.

Printed in the United States of America

ISBN 0-88671-497-4 (Previously ISBN 0-7916-0103-X)

Order Number: 80250

A 0 9 8 7 6

Contents

Preface

Health ranks as a number one topic of conversation and interest in the lives of people. From prenatal care to matters of concern in old age, health plays a large role in today's society. Modern health focuses on wellness and on the prevention of disease. These are major reasons for studying health.

The study of health leads to an awareness of good health practices. Such practices involve a life-style that values physical and mental fitness. Measures are based on knowledge of body systems, proper exercise and nutrition, and the nature of diseases and disorders and their care and treatment.

Purposes of This Book

Basic Health presents the most important ideas in the study of health directly and in plain language. Decision-making is emphasized as the key factor in getting, maintaining, and directing personal health. Health is very much a personal matter. The book puts ideas in clear language and essential detail. It attempts to satisfy student curiosity and interest. The subject matter is intended to stimulate conversation and lead to further reading. Students are encouraged to ask questions and to seek help from their counselor, teacher, minister, social worker, and friends as the need arises.

Organization of the Book

This textbook is made up of thirteen chapters. Each chapter can stand alone as a topic of study and discussion. The chapters are organized around chapter goals and are divided into sections focused on key ideas. At the end of each key idea section there is a set of questions to check understanding.

Chapter Conclusions

At the conclusion of each chapter there is a summary and a list of important words used in the chapter. The final exercise of the chapter is an extensive set of review questions. By answering these questions, students can determine if they have mastered the main ideas in the chapter.

Vocabulary

The main concepts of health are presented in clear and simple language. The book is easy to read because of the large type, the generous headings, the short sentences, and the brief paragraphs. Essential health information is included, yet an effort has been made to use familiar words and a comfortable writing style.

Teacher's Guide

The Teacher's Guide and Answer Key that accompanies this textbook contains an overview of each chapter, objectives, answers to the questions, and teaching suggestions. In addition, there are reproducible chapter tests and supplementary student activity pages.

Student Workbook

The accompanying student workbook provides additional practice activities that review and reinforce the topics presented in the textbook.

CHAPTER GOALS:

To define health.

To describe factors that influence health.

KEY IDEAS:

Health is wellness. Health is related to life-style.

Health is based on uniqueness of the individual. Heredity, environment, life-style, and personality provide the differences among people.

Health has three major branches: physical well-being, mental or emotional well-being, and social well-being.

Health is a process of getting to know yourself, recognizing a self-image, and developing a personality.

Health is centered around basic life functions that take place in cells, organs, and body systems.

Heredity and environment are key factors in determining health.

What Makes You You

KEY IDEA #1:
Health is wellness. Health is related to life-style.

Health

"How are you today?" may be the most frequently asked question in the world.

"I'm fine, thank you" may be the most common answer.

When someone asks how you are, the question is really aimed at asking about your **health**. Your health is made up of your physical well-being, your mental or emotional well-being, and your social well-being. So, when you tell others that you are fine, you really are saying a lot in just a few words.

"I'm fine" could mean that you are physically fit, in a good mental or emotional state, and able to get along well with everybody. Your answer to the question, "How are you today?" is a description of your **wellness**.

Describing Wellness

Wellness can be described in a general manner. People have their own ways of telling others about the level of their well-being. For example, a friend might say to you, "I'm about a six or a seven today." He means that his well-being is just about at the middle on a scale of one to ten. Though he does not feel great, he does not feel too badly, either.

Most people have a range of wellness that stays fairly even from day to day. Some people, on the other hand, seem to feel badly all the time. Others may always be "just great" or "on top of the world."

In the past, having good health meant being free from disease. Modern health study, however, focuses on the idea of wellness. Today, a person's **life-style** is considered to be a key factor in being healthy! What a person does day by day is what makes a life-style. Each person develops a distinct life-style.

CHECK YOUR UNDERSTANDING

1. When people say "How are you today?" what are they aking about?
2. When asked "How are you today?" what do you usually say?
3. Why are people so interested in the way others feel?
4. On a list of things to be concerned about, where do you place your health? Explain your choice.
5. What is the study of health all about?

KEY IDEA #2:
Health is based on uniqueness of the individual.
Heredity, environment, life-style, and personality
provide the differences among people.

A Look at Yourself

Who Are You?

To start with, you are unique—"a single copy." There is no one in the entire world exactly like you. Of course, there are some people around you who are very much like you. They are your mother and father. You may also have brothers and sisters and grandmothers and grandfathers. You resemble your relatives because of **heredity**. Heredity is the passing of characteristics, or traits, from parents to children. Traits such as the way you look, the ways that you behave, and your mannerisms are **inherited traits**.

Environment

Who you are is the result of a combination of your inherited traits and your **environment**. Your environment is the set of conditions in which you live. It has had an effect on the way you grow up. Now and in the future, your environment will help to determine who you become.

Life-style

Your health is partly a result of what you inherited from your parents and grandparents. Your health also depends on things that you have done and are doing. Health is an ongoing process rather than a thing. It depends on the environment that you provide for your body and for your mind. How you live day by day, month by month, and year by year is called your life-style. You make personal choices that determine your life-style. Therefore, you make choices that influence your health.

Your Personality

Being with your family puts you in close contact with people like yourself. This close contact gives you a feeling of belonging. Belonging with others and spending time with them add to your sense of well-being. Within the family, however, you remain unique. You are one of a kind. You have your own **personality**. Your personality is a combination of what you are, what you do, and when, how, and why you do those things.

You—The Decision Maker

"I'd like to decide that for myself!" you say. Much of what happens in your life happens as a result of the decisions you make. Living is a decision-making process. Your health is affected by these decisions.

The following example shows just how much you are personally in charge of your own health. "Should I brush my teeth once a day, twice a day, every other day, or not at all?" you ask. The choice is yours to make. A wise choice will improve your health. Your state of well-being depends on the condition of your gums and teeth. Though your decision may not seem like such a big deal, it is important.

Here is another example:

"Should I smoke, or not smoke?" Read the warning on the label of a pack of cigarettes—Surgeon General's Warning: Quitting Smoking Now Greatly Reduces Serious Risks To Your Health.

The smoking decision, like the teeth-brushing one, is

an individual matter. You will have to make these kinds of decisions every day of your life. Clearly, you are in control as the decision maker. Making good decisions is one of the best ways to stay healthy.

SURGEON GENERAL'S WARNING: Quitting Smoking Now Greatly Reduces Serious Risks To Your Health.

Twin Towers

CHECK YOUR UNDERSTANDING

1. Describe what it means to be unique.

2. Define heredity.

3. What else, besides heredity, helps answer the question, "Who am I?"

4. How does a person's life-style influence health?

5. List some of the things that make up a person's personality.

6. What part does decision making play in matters about health?

7. Write a brief description of a situation in which you made a decision.

Well-Being

Physical Well-Being

Maintaining your physical condition involves eating well, exercising, and getting proper rest. It also involves good dental hygiene, cleanliness, and proper care of your hair, skin, and nails. Just being aware of your physical condition takes very little effort on your part. Doing the tasks to take care of yourself is what takes time and effort. Your **physical well-being** is the reward.

Mental or Emotional Well-Being

Feeling good because of your physical efforts can lead to **mental well-being**. Mental or emotional well-being is not as easy to see or to be aware of as physical well-being, but it is just as important. With practice, you can be more aware of your mental or emotional condition. Do you enjoy a variety of activities? Do you have an optimistic outlook? Are you more positive than negative in your thinking? Being optimistic and having a positive attitude will add to your mental well-being.

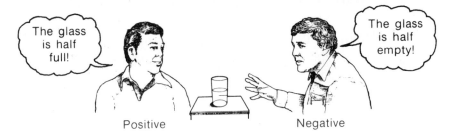

Positive   Negative

Social Well-Being

Your physical and mental well-being set the stage for your **social well-being**. Your social health begins with getting along with yourself. You must see yourself as a positive person, in control of your physical well-being. You will be able to do things that are needed to get along with others. Getting along with other people and with yourself is social well-being.

It is not always easy to keep it all together. You must be aware that it takes effort. The reward for working to get and maintain physical, mental, and social well-being is good health. Most people would agree that good health is priceless.

CHECK YOUR UNDERSTANDING

1. Give an example of decision making that promotes good health.
2. List the three main branches of being healthy.
3. What is it that leads to physical well-being?
4. How is mental or emotional well-being achieved?
5. What are some things that add to your social well-being?

KEY IDEA #4:
Health is a process of getting to know yourself,
recognizing a self-image, and developing a
personality.

To Know Yourself

Getting to know yourself is an important part of being healthy. It takes extra effort for any person to know more about who and what they are. Knowing yourself means being able to answer some basic questions: Do you like yourself? Do you do things just for yourself and never think of others? Do you get angry often? Do you express your anger in physical ways—punching, breaking, throwing, or shouting? Do you think about the source of your anger? Do you find out what part you played in bringing on your feelings of anger?

A searching and questioning attitude is important in getting to know yourself. Wanting to learn about your emotions, about how you handle stress, and about how you act and react to your own feelings of anger can help you to know yourself.

Self-Image

Getting to know yourself is something to be concerned about. You need to be able to live within yourself. To do that, you must develop a positive **self-image**. A self-image involves picturing in your mind the way you behave and think. Do you see yourself as a pleasant, happy, upbeat person?

Or do you see yourself as the opposite—an unpleasant, unhappy, discontented, and downbeat person? Do you see yourself changing back and forth between one kind of person one day and a different kind of person another day? Answering these kinds of questions will give you a set of ideas about who and what you are. This is your self-image.

Building a Positive Self-Image

What are some traits or **characteristics** that lead an individual to have a positive image? Do words like dependable, responsible, caring, loving, honest, reliable, friendly, helpful, and trustworthy pop into your head? Do you think of yourself as a hard worker, a team player, a leader?

A person's self-image plays a big part in daily life. To be useful, a strong self-image must be nourished. It requires daily care and attention. A person's self-image is reflected in dealings with other people. If you have a strong self-image, people see you as confident and sincere. Self-image shows on the outside as your **personality.**

CHECK YOUR UNDERSTANDING

1. Make a list of questions you should ask when you try to know yourself.
2. Describe self-image.
3. What are some words you could use to describe a person who has a positive self-image?

Basic Life Functions

Cells are the microscopic basic units of the human body. They make up different kinds of **body tissues**. These tissues can be muscle tissue, nerve tissue, bone tissue, connective tissue, and blood tissue. Some cells are lining cells. Your digestive organs—the stomach, small intestine, and large intestine—are lined with cells. Cells are one of the marvels of nature. They carry out many different jobs. Muscle cells expand and contract. Nerve cells send and receive electrochemical signals called impulses. In the brain, cells store the information that is used to put together thoughts and ideas. In the bloodstream, cells are specialized to carry oxygen and carbon dioxide to and from all parts of the body.

Health depends on the proper working of the cells. Some causes of poor health are tied directly to the improper working of cells. Cancer is one example of a disease where cells do not function properly. Certain heart conditions happen because cells fail to work properly.

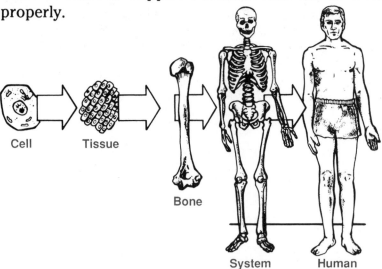

Cell   Tissue

Bone

System   Human

Cells are the basic units of your body structure. They are the building blocks of the body. They also are the working units of your body. Cells get the job done. They are the basic units of health.

Body Organs

The **organs** in the body are made up of cells and tissues that work together. The **heart** is an organ that is made up of different kinds of **tissues**. Muscle cells make up the heart's muscle tissue. Nerve cells make up the heart's nerve tissue. **Connective tissue** is made of special cells that hold the other tissue together. Parts of the heart—muscles, blood vessels, connective tissue, nerve tissue, and the blood itself—are all in the right place at the right time. They work together, controlled by chemicals found in each of the different kinds of cells. The heart and other body organs are **organized** sets of cells. Each body organ has a certain job to do. Your overall health, or condition of well-being, is tied to how well your body parts are working. Health problems can be connected to certain organs.

Body Systems

The human body is organized into **body systems**. Humans are called **organisms**. So are horses, cats, mules, and elephants. All of these animals have body systems that coordinate the body's work. The major work of the body is to stay healthy. The body does this by carrying out **basic life functions**. Breathing, eating food, moving, and responding are basic life functions. The basic life functions are carried out by the following body systems:

1. The muscular system
2. The nervous system
3. The circulatory system
4. The digestive system
5. The respiratory system
6. The skeletal system

7. The endocrine system

8. The excretory system

9. The reproductive system

Even though the systems of the body can be listed separately, the body systems do not work separately. The body systems work together as a total organism. The systems keep the body working and keep it healthy. You should notice that the words organism and organization have the same beginning letters: o-r-g-a-n. A church organ fits the same kind of description as a body organ. Each kind of organ is a set of parts working together. The church organ produces good music. The body organs produce good health. Football teams are also made up of separate parts that work together. A team is organized if the parts play well together. Church organs, sports teams, and body systems are all organized to perform certain jobs.

You might ask, "What do the body systems have to do with the study of health?" The answer should help you with your thinking and organizing of ideas about health. The body systems play a big part in the definition of health. Earlier we described health as physical well-being, mental well-being, and social well-being. Systems of the body are at work in all of these three branches of health. The physical, mental and social parts must work together to maintain health. Keeping the body systems in working order requires good daily health habits.

1. Define cells.

2. List some different kinds of cells.

3. How does the heart qualify as an organ?

4. List some basic life functions.

5. List four of the body systems that carry on basic life functions.

6. What part do organs play in human health?

7. List the three parts of health that depend on the human body system.

KEY IDEA #6:

Heredity and environment are key factors in determining health.

Genetics and Health

Genetics is the science of genes, chromosomes, and heredity. **Genes** are known as the material of heredity. Genes produce traits like eye color. Heredity is the study of how traits are passed from parents to children.

Genes Are a Family Affair

Human life begins as a single cell. That single cell is made by the joining of a male sperm cell and a female egg cell. **Sperm** and **eggs** are reproductive cells. One-half of the baby's genes come from the mother. The other one-half comes from the father. Genes are very powerful. Genes influence traits such as hair color, height and weight, tone and quality of the voice, shape and size of the nose, and eye color. Sometimes athletic ability runs in families. Sometimes musical talent runs in families. Can you think of other examples?

Health and the Genes

Health patterns also run in families. Families include mothers and fathers, sisters and brothers, grandmothers

---

and grandfathers, aunts and uncles, and cousins. Genes are a connecting link between relatives. Genes cause health traits to run in families. This is why doctors are interested in the health record of your family when they give you a physical examination. It helps them complete your health picture.

Four brothers are all talented singers.

Genes and Chromosomes

One of the characteristics that is passed on from the parents is the sex of the child. Genes determine the sex of the baby.

Males have an **X chromosome** and a **Y chromosome** in their reproductive cells. Chromosomes are very thin structures that carry the genes. Males carry the X and Y chromosomes. A male cell can be shown as an XY. The X and Y are symbols that stand for the genetic material of a male.

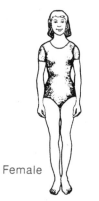

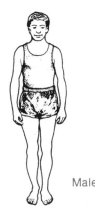

Females have only X chromosomes. A female egg cell can be shown as XX. When single eggs are formed before fertilization takes place, the egg is shown as an X. Females produce eggs with only an X chromosome.

Female
Male

XX Chromosomes   XY Chromosomes

Fertilization is the joining of an egg cell and a sperm cell. When fertilization takes place, the male sperm carries either an X or a Y chromosome. The female can contribute only X chromosomes.

Look at the diagram below. It shows the chromosomes that come from the male and the female.

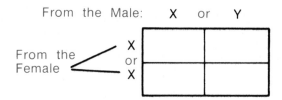

If fertilization occurs, the baby's sex could be any of the choices that appear in the chart below. XX stands for female babies, and XY stands for male babies.

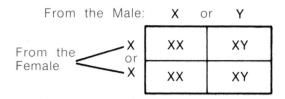

Genes also control many other human traits, including hair color, eye color, general body shape, and other traits that make people alike or different.

Genes are not the only factors that contribute to your uniqueness. Another important factor is the environment in which each individual lives.

CHECK YOUR UNDERSTANDING

1. What are genes?
2. List some traits or characteristics that are influenced by genes.
3. How do genes cause similarities between family members?
4. What part do genes play in determining the sex of a baby?
5. How does environment influence the health of humans?

Summary of Chapter 1

Health is a subject of great interest to us all. People have always been interested in their own bodies, minds, and personalities. Health is about physical well-being, mental well-being, and social well-being. The study of health starts with who you are. You learn that you are unique because of heredity and your environment, lifestyle, and personality. Health is about wellness and lifestyle.

Humans are unique in their decision-making ability. The decisions you make are important factors in determining the state of your health, now and in the future. Heredity is also a major factor in health. Your environment plays a key role as well. Physical, mental, and social health all are tied together in each person's life to determine their wellness. Getting to know yourself provides you with a self-image. Self-image plays a major role in social well-being. Personality development and self-image go hand in hand.

Humans are influenced by their genes. Genes give direction to the development of organs and body systems. Heredity works through genes. It plays a large part in determining an individual's health. Health patterns, as determined by genes, sometimes run in families.

WORDS TO USE

1. health
2. wellness
3. inherited traits
4. environment
5. life-style
6. physical well-being
7. mental well-being
8. social well-being
9. self-image
10. personality
11. characteristics
12. cells
13. body tissues
14. organs
15. heart
16. tissues
17. connective tissues
18. body systems
19. organisms
20. basic life functions
21. organized
22. genetics
23. genes
24. heredity
25. sperm
26. eggs
27. X chromosome
28. Y chromosome

REVIEW QUESTIONS FOR CHAPTER 1

1. When you answer the question, "How are you today?" what are you describing?

2. How has the definition of having good health changed over the years?

3. Define heredity.

4. What makes each person unique?

5. Describe the role that environment plays in determining who you are.

6. Give two examples of decisions you made today that will influence your health.

7. List four things you do every day to maintain your physical well-being.

8. Name two branches of health that contribute to your social well-being.

9. How can you find out more about yourself?

10. Why is it important to have a positive self-image?

11. Describe the work of the cells in your brain.

12. List the basic systems that carry out the body's basic life functions.

13. Define a body organ. Give two examples of organs in the human body.

14. Why do some family members share some of the same characteristics?

15. What part do the genes play in determining your health?

CHAPTER GOALS:

To understand the role of adolescence in humans.

To realize that a healthy adolescence involves body changes, problem-solving, and becoming mature.

KEY IDEAS:

Body changes are a major feature of the adolescent years.

The teenage years bring a special set of problems common to adolescents.

Becoming mature is a major step toward a healthy life-style.

CHAPTER 2

Adolescence and Health

Adolescence is a word used to describe a period in the life of humans. It is a time for growing. An **adolescent** is a human being at a stage between childhood and adulthood. When you are an adolescent, there are many changes in your life. One of the changes is just growing—getting larger through physical change. Other changes are taking place in your mental growth. You are developing greater thinking and reasoning skills.

The time frame of adolescence is unique in humans. No other animals have such a long period of growing up. Humans usually go through adolescence during their teen years—ages thirteen through nineteen. There are exceptions, though. Some people enter adolescence at eleven. Some stay in this period through age twenty. Adolescence is not a fixed time. Each person enters and leaves this period according to his or her own body's schedule. However, most of the body's physical change and growth during adolescence takes place over a span of about four years.

As you go through adolescence, much of your living is done by trial and error. You are no longer under someone's constant care as you were in childhood. Yet you have not reached the time of much greater independence—young adulthood.

During adolescence, some characteristic body changes take place. Your body grows and develops. There are behavior changes. These are tied closely to personality development, family living, and social development. Another key happening in the teen years is an increase in the number and scope of the adolescent's responsibilities. These years are a time for practicing decision-making skills about health.

KEY IDEA #1:
Body changes are a major feature of the adolescent years.

Body Changes

Growth and change are normal events in the life of a human. Most growth is slow and gradual. Humans get taller, heavier, and change shape over long periods. Some growth takes place very rapidly, with changes occurring in spurts. This is the way growth happens in adolescence. From about age eleven for girls and age twelve for boys, body changes happen that move a person from childhood toward adulthood. The growth and change an adolescent feels and sees are normal parts of growing up.

Hormones and Glands

Much of our body changes are controlled by **hormones.** Hormones are chemicals that are formed in special body structures called **glands.** The glands release the hormones into the bloodstream. As the hormones travel about the body, they cause certain body parts to start growing or speed up their growth. Hormones can also cause some body parts to change.

The master gland is the **pituitary gland**. It is found at the base of the brain. The pituitary gland is called the "master gland" because it sends out hormones that control the actions of other glands.

Pituitary hormones act as chemical messengers to tell other glands in the body to start releasing their hormones. Your body is under the control of this gland system. Through your life, this system acts to control the rates, or speed, of body activities.

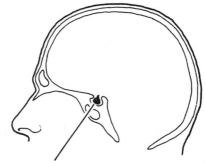

The pituitary gland releases hormones.

Boys and girls experience a period of rapid growth during their adolescence. In general, girls begin their growth spurts at the age of eleven or twelve. They grow taller and heavier. This change is caused by hormones released from the gland system, headed by the pituitary. Boys also experience a growth spurt during adolescence. It is also triggered by the gland system. This growth generally starts around age fourteen. Both boys and girls continue to grow rapidly until about age eighteen.

Adults often describe their growing teenagers as "gangly." Arms, legs, hands, and feet seem to go in all directions. It is normal for adolescents to be gangly. Your arms, legs, hands, and feet often grow to adult size before the rest of your body parts do.

Sometimes, adolescents are uncomfortable with the body changes that happen. Because the boys' growth spurt usually occurs later than the growth spurt in girls, it may seem as if the girls are "ahead" of the boys. This difference among teenagers existed for years and years before you became a teenager yourself. Differences among individuals—in size, shape, and time of development—cause some adolescents to worry that they are not normal. Fortunately, this concern goes away with time. Most adults can look back and recall that these differences bothered them while they were teenagers.

The changes that take place during adolescence don't happen the same way to everyone. But they do follow patterns that can be described. Knowing something about these patterns is useful in dealing with the growth spurts and other physical changes that take place during the teen years.

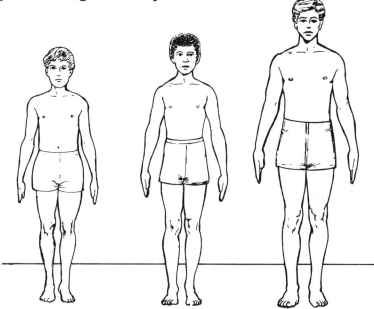

Three fourteen-year-old boys are very different in their development.

Males at Puberty

Puberty is a word that comes from the Latin word *puber,* which means "of ripe age." During puberty, the sex organs and glands begin to work. Males and females at this stage in life are now able to reproduce. We can say that they are now **sexually mature**.

Between the ages of twelve and fifteen, the **reproductive systems** of most boys begin to work. This means that the male **sex glands** begin to make sperm. Sperm are sex cells that are made in the **testes**. The testes are the male reproductive glands. Besides making sperm, the testes also make the hormone **testosterone**. This hormone sets in motion changes in the body that result in hair growth on the face, under the arms, and in the **genital** area. Genitals are external sex organs. Testosterone is also responsible for a deepening of the voice and an increase in the size or mass of muscles in the chest, arms, and legs.

The amount of testosterone that is released varies among individuals. Some boys' bodies manufacture more testosterone than other boys' bodies. Some boys' bodies produce testosterone at an earlier age. These are some of the main reasons that there is such a wide range in the size and general appearance of boys who are the same age. In one classroom full of fourteen-year-olds, there may be tall and short boys, fuzzy-faced and smooth-skinned ones, broad- and narrow-shouldered boys, boys who are muscular, and ones who are not so muscular. In that same classroom, a range of voices, from very deep basses to high-pitched altos, may be heard.

Between the ages of twelve and eighteen, males come in all sizes and stages of physical **maturity**.

Puberty in Females

Most females go through puberty at an earlier age than their male classmates. Puberty is that time period when sexual maturity is reached. In girls, puberty usually occurs between the ages of eleven and fourteen. Triggered by hormones, the **ovaries** grow and develop. The ovaries are female **reproductive organs**. **Egg cells** are produced in the ovaries. The ovaries also produce a hormone called **estrogen**. Estrogen causes other changes to take place. These include breast development, widening of the hips, and an increase in height and weight. Other hormones cause hair to grow in the genital area and under the arms. Girls also begin to menstruate during this time. Not all girls undergo these changes at the same rate. But, they do go through the same pattern of growth and development.

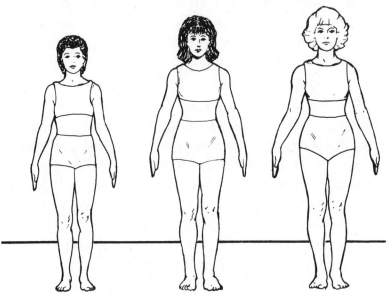

Three twelve-year-old girls differ in their development.

CHECK YOUR UNDERSTANDING

1. Define the term *"adolescent."*
2. What makes the human adolescent period unique?
3. List three categories of key events that occur during the teen years.
4. How is growth different during the teen years?
5. Define hormones.
6. Which gland is called the master gland?
7. What causes an adolescent to look gangly?
8. What does the word *puberty* mean?
9. Describe the role testosterone plays in a boy's development.
10. List some changes that take place in females at the time of puberty.

Basic Health

The teenage years bring a special set of problems
common to adolescents.

Problems for Teenagers

How are you today? Are you "up," "down," or
somewhere in between? The way you "are" has to do
with your **emotions.** Emotions are the way you feel. The
way you feel is the result of what you do and what
happens to you. If you are feeling up today, it could be
that something has happened to give you
pleasure or joy. Maybe you have had a pleasant
surprise, such as a telephone call from a friend
who had moved to another city. Perhaps you
are proud of a science project that was one of
the best in the class.

Stress

Feelings of ups and downs are normal for the teen
years. This emotional roller coaster is caused, in some
part, by the bodily changes described earlier in this
chapter.

Being down can cause a condition called **stress.** Stress
is the set of physical and emotional reactions we have
when we feel we are under pressure. What are some
everyday events and situations in a teenager's life that
can cause stress? You can make your own list.

Every day brings some kind and some degree of
stress. Some stress and emotional strain is normal. But
when stressful events pile up or a stressful situation
continues for a long time, you may start to feel restless,
tense, or tired. You may not be able to sleep or make a
decision. You may lose interest in school, church, or
your home. These are signs that need special attention.
You will need to look for ways to reduce the stress that
is causing your physical problems.

Range of Stress

Metals used to build bridges, skyscrapers, airplanes, and automobiles are subjected to stress tests. These stress tests measure the amount of push, pull, or stretch that these building materials can handle without breaking apart. Just as the metal will respond to a range of stress, so, too, will humans. Often, people conduct their own stress tests. From experience, an individual can usually tell how much stress can be handled before a breakdown. Most humans learn to adjust to certain amounts of daily stress. Stress is built into most job and life situations. We need to be able to deal with stress. Adolescence is a time for learning how to handle daily stress.

Bridges can withstand a great deal of stress.

Much of the stress felt during the teen years is due to chemical and physical changes. These changes happen to all teenagers. It is good for you to remember that you are not the only one who feels stress when you are dealing with these changes. Other adolescents—your friends and classmates—are also dealing with the same kinds of stress.

You could write a long list of stressful events that every teen has to handle. Schoolwork and school activities are among the leading causes of stress in teens. School is a place for doing work and a place for having fun. It is also a place for growing up. The situation is complicated because so many other people are involved. First and foremost, there you are, getting up early every day, getting ready for school, doing your chores at home, leaving the house on time, and settling into your school day. None of this is done in a vacuum. Your parents, sisters, brothers, friends, classmates, and teachers all place demands, obligations, and expectations on you. The interactions of all these people form your individual **stress network**.

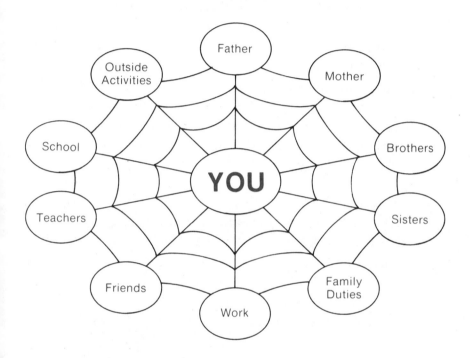

Stress places mental and physical demands on you. You are expected to behave in certain ways that are often established by other people. For example, you are expected to be on time, to get good grades, and to keep your room neat and clean. The stress that results from doing all these things is a normal part of life. This kind of stress causes you to get your work done on time, and to do it well enough to satisfy or please you. This kind of stress can keep you on your toes and cause you to do your best. Most of a teenager's daily routine is carried out under a range of pressure or stress that is acceptable and workable for the individual.

However, some events in life can cause more stress and pressure than a person is accustomed to handling. These are usually events that a person cannot control. Events such as the death of a close relative, friend, or classmate would cause an extreme amount of stress. Other examples of things that cause stress are parents' separation or divorce, or a friend or relative who has a serious health problem, or who is addicted to drugs or alcohol. Studies about the effect of stress on humans put events like these on the top of the list of most stressful events. These conditions cannot be controlled by the individual. They are the most difficult conditions to handle. Teens deal with stressful situations related to their own behavior, or under their own control, with much more success.

Learning to Cope

The adolescent years are a time to grow and learn how to **cope**. Coping means handling a situation while continuing to lead a normal life. Teenagers get practice in coping with many stressful situations, such as breaking up with a boyfriend or girlfriend. A breakup is a stressful event that often seems like the end of the world. Learning to deal with events like this, and the stress they cause, is something all teenagers do.

Luckily, teens have groups of people to rely on when they reach the end of the range of stress that they can handle. Parents and relatives, teachers, classmates, friends, and the clergy all want to help teenagers through adolescence. This group of people is known as an **adolescent support team**. This team has learned from experience to help the stressed person to make a plan that will ease the stress. The person who is a good, supportive listener is the most helpful member of this team. In the eyes of a teenager, the person who is the least helpful is the one who preaches, scolds, or is quick to place blame.

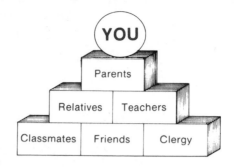

YOU

Parents

Relatives | Teachers

Classmates | Friends | Clergy

Seeking and Getting Help

Experience has shown that the biggest help any member of a support team gives is making the teenager feel loved and not alone.

A girl named Sandra got that kind of help from a **peer counselor**. A peer counselor is a person in your own age group who can help you examine a problem. When Sandra's father died, she went to talk with a peer counselor. Sandra's counselor was a student at her school. Sandra told her counselor that she felt the worst when she saw her mother cry. The counselor reassured her that other families had experiences just like "the ones your family went through."

Influences on Behavior

The way teenagers behave is closely tied to their parents' **value system**. Years of influence in the home result in a strong relationship between beliefs and values in the home and a teenager's behavior. Parents and other adults have the strongest influence on teenagers.

Teenagers also influence each other. The day-to-day interactions among teens are subject to **peer pressure**. An adolescent makes certain decisions based on the way friends and classmates feel or react. Decisions influenced by peer pressure are very common.

Another major factor that influences a teen's behavior choices is a sense of fair play.

Pressure from the home value system and peer pressure from friends or classmates, filtered through a sense of fair play, shape many decision-making behaviors of adolesents.

1. Define the term *"emotions."*
2. What is stress?
3. Describe some possible results of long-term stress.
4. Give the meaning of the word *"cope."*
5. What kinds of pressure influence a teenager's behavior?

KEY IDEA #3:

Becoming mature is a major step toward a healthy life-style.

Gaining Maturity

During adolescence, an individual takes many steps toward maturity. A mature person is one who has completed natural growth and development. Becoming mature involves developing or acquiring useful personal and behavioral characteristics. Think about your own level of maturity. Do you set realistic goals? Setting realistic goals is one sign of maturity. Being able to set goals that can be reached is a desirable characteristic.

Decision Making

Setting goals involves **decision making**. Decision making is a process. In order to make decisions, you need to gather useful information. Using this information, step by step, in making decisions is something you learn. During adolescence, you are given more and more chances to use the decision-making process.

The ability to make sound decisions varies from one individual to the next. One person you know may be a good decision maker. Another may be a poor one. Making wise decisions or good choices about your own actions is part of becoming mature. On their way to maturity, most teenagers make some poor decisions.

Mistakes allow teens to learn. The teen years are a time for learning and a time for growing. As we grow older, maturity and experience are expected to lead to fewer and fewer mistakes.

Responsibility

Another part of becoming mature is learning to be responsible. Everyone must deal with responsibility. Society is built on the idea of individual responsibility. Some people measure maturity by the level of an individual's sense of responsibility. The adolescent years are a time when there is a shift toward increased responsibility. You may have already noticed that people expect more from you than they did when you were younger. You are also being placed in more and more situations in which you must make your own decisions. Parents, teachers, and other adults provide many new opportunities for the teenagers in their lives to practice

handling an increasing amount of responsibility.

Decision making and responsibility are characteristics that have a great deal to do with the way you feel about yourself. Whether you realize it or not, making decisions and developing responsibility are something that you do every day in many small ways. For example, you might have only fifty cents in your pocket. You need to get home on time. But you also want a soda. Bus fare and soda each cost fifty cents. What would your decision be? Is that a responsible decision? As a teenager, you can see that your actions affect your life. You are making decisions about how to react to all kinds of people and events. Practice at decision making will help you become responsible.

Adolescence is a time for beginning a **philosophy of life**. A philosophy is a personal way of looking at the world and the way it works and the way you feel it should work. During your teen years, you begin shaping your own **life-style** based on a philosophy of life. A life-style is your way of life and is based on decisions you have made about what is important to you.

Self-Concept

As a teenager, you make decisions and take on new responsibilities. When you evaluate your decision-making ability and your ability to handle responsibility, you are forming a **self-concept**. A self-concept is the picture you have of yourself. Self-concept has a great deal to do with the way you see yourself in school, in dealings with other people, and in your family role. Are you confident that you can deal with most situations? Do you enjoy doing things at school and with other people? Do you join in and take your share of responsibility? Do you feel comfortable as part of a group? Do you trust yourself? Do you accept and trust your friends? The answers to these questions will give you an idea of your own self- concept.

CHECK YOUR UNDERSTANDING
1. Define maturity.
2. What is involved in making a decision?
3. What part does decision making play during the teenage years?
4. What is a self-concept?
5. How does your sense of responsibility affect your self-concept?

Summary of Chapter 2

The period of life called adolescence is a special time. Adolescents grow from childhood to adulthood, both physically and emotionally. Adolescence is a period when bodies change, special problems arise, and maturation takes place. The glands of the body produce hormones that control growth and rates of change. Boys and girls have different patterns and rates of growth. Because of this difference, the appearance of members of the same age group can differ widely. Puberty is the period when both males and females mature sexually; their reproductive systems begin to work.

Emotions cause a wide range of ups and downs. Some long-term down feelings lead to stress. Stress is a normal part of living. Most people learn how to deal with stress during their teens. Dealing with stress and other pressures allows teenagers a chance to learn how to cope. The teen years are recognized as a time for learning through experience. Adolescent support teams made up of friends, parents, teachers, classmates, relatives, and clergy give comfort, direction, and assistance.

Maturity is a natural outcome of teenage growth and development. Personal character is developed through daily decision-making opportunities. Development of a sense of responsibility is characteristic of the teen years. The beginnings of a philosophy of life are established, and a self-concept is developed.

WORDS TO USE

1. adolescent
2. hormones
3. glands
4. pituitary gland
5. puberty
6. reproductive system
7. sex glands
8. testes
9. testosterone
10. genital
11. ovaries
12. reproductive organs
13. sexually mature
14. egg cells
15. estrogen
16. emotions
17. stress
18. stress network
19. cope
20. adolescent support team
21. peer counselor
22. value system
23. peer pressure
24. maturity
25. decision making
26. philosophy of life
27. life-style
28. self-concept
29. adolescence

REVIEW QUESTIONS FOR CHAPTER 2

1. What are some of the changes that take place during adolescence?

2. List some key events of the teen years.

3. How does a child's growth rate change during the teen years?

4. Describe what hormones do for the body.

5. What does the gland system do?

6. List some ways in which teenagers vary.

7. What is puberty?

8. Name three characteristics of boys at puberty.

9. Name three characteristics of girls at puberty.

10. Why are thirteen-year-old girls usually taller than boys their age?

11. What is the definition of emotions?

12. What is stress?

13. List some causes of extreme stress in the lives of teenagers.

14. What is a stress network?

15. When is stress normal?

16. Why should you learn to cope with stressful situations?

17. What value system is most accepted by teenagers?

18. Describe what happens when a person reaches maturity.

19. What does the decision-making process involve?

20. What is the meaning of the term *self-concept*?

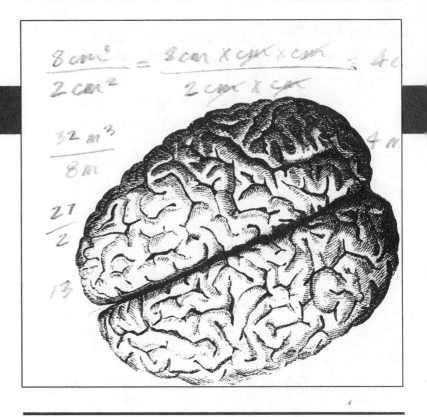

CHAPTER GOALS:

To describe how the nervous system and the sense organs send and receive information in order to control and coordinate the body.

To identify some health problems of the nervous system and sense organs.

KEY IDEAS:

The brain, spinal cord, and peripheral nerves make up the nervous system. The nervous system relays messages and tells the body what to do.

Problems of the nervous system range from common headaches to serious brain disorders.

The eyes, ears, nose, tongue, and skin are sense organs that receive information.

Problems of the eyes and ears include varying degrees of blindness and hearing loss.

CHAPTER 3

The Nervous System and the Sense Organs

KEY IDEA #1:
The brain, the spinal cord, and the peripheral nerves make up the nervous system. The nervous system relays messages and tells the body what to do.

The Brain and Its Cocaptains

You probably already know that the **brain** controls the body's actions. The brain is like the captain of a ship. Like a good ship's captain, the brain needs cocaptains to help steer the ship on a safe course.

The brain's cocaptains are the **spinal cord** and the **peripheral nerves**. Each of these parts needs the other two in order to function. The brain, the spinal cord, and the peripheral nerves work together to make up the body's nervous system.

The Brain

The three main parts of the brain are the **cerebrum**, the **cerebellum**, and the **brain stem.** The cerebrum is the largest part of the brain. It is the part of the brain that enables you to read, think, and remember.

The cerebrum is divided into two halves, called hemispheres. The right hemisphere controls activities on the left side of the body. The left hemisphere controls activities on the right side. In addition, each hemisphere is specialized. The right hemisphere is connected with artistic matters and intuitive thinking. The left hemisphere deals with math, language, and logical thinking.

The other two parts of the brain are much smaller than the cerebrum. The cerebellum lies between the cerebrum and the brain stem. It controls balance and helps coordinate muscular activities, such as walking and running.

The brain stem connects the brain with the spinal cord. One part of the brain stem is called the **medulla**. The medulla controls your body's **automatic activities**. These are the things your body does without thinking, like digesting food, circulating blood, and breathing.

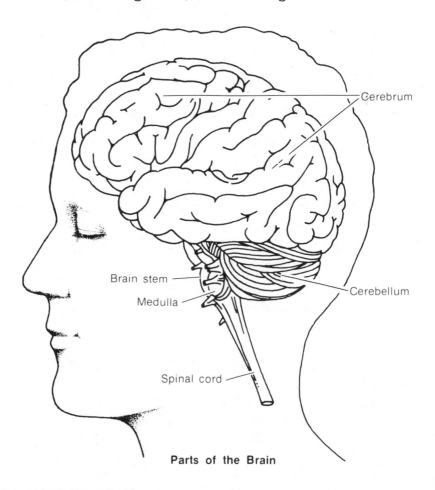

Cerebrum

Brain stem

Medulla

Cerebellum

Spinal cord

Parts of the Brain

The Spinal Cord

To help you imagine what the spinal cord is like, think of a thick telephone cable. A cable is a bunch of wires wound together. In the same way, the spinal cord is a bunch of very long nerve cells that are twisted together.

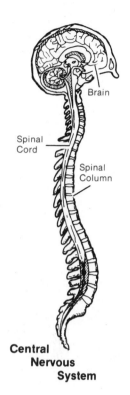

The spinal cord connects to the brain stem and goes down to the lower part of the back. The spinal column, a series of small bones, surrounds the spinal cord. It protects the spinal cord. If the nerves that make up the spinal cord are damaged, they cannot repair themselves. Any cut in the spinal cord results in **paralysis** in parts of the body that are at or below the point where the cut is. When a body part becomes paralyzed, a person loses the ability to move that part.

Sending Messages

The nerves that make up the spinal cord act like telephone wires. They receive messages from the brain and relay them to another set of nerves called peripheral nerves. Peripheral nerves carry all the messages sent between the **central nervous system** and the rest of the body. The brain and the spinal cord make up the central nervous system.

The Autonomic Nervous System

One part of the peripheral nerve system also helps regulate your body's automatic processes. It is called the **autonomic nervous system**. Its actions are already programmed to help the body. It speeds up the body's processes, like breathing and heartbeat, when there is an emergency. The autonomic nervous system also slows down the body's processes when the emergency has passed or the body is at rest.

Reflexes

There is a special part of the peripheral nervous system that controls your **reflexes**. Reflexes are automatic reactions to a stimulus, such as heat or pain. For example, when you touch a hot pot, your hand jerks away, even before you have had a chance to think about it. When you touch that pot, your nerves send a message to the muscles of the hand. This happens rapidly. The message says, "Pull your hand away immediately."

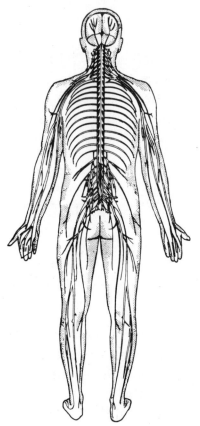

Peripheral Nervous System

CHECK YOUR UNDERSTANDING

1. Name three parts of the nervous system.
2. What does the cerebellum do?
3. What is the medulla?
4. List some activities that are controlled by the autonomic nervous system.
5. How does a reflex work?

Problems of the nervous system range from the common headache to serious brain disorders.

Headaches and Other Disorders

The next time you watch television, keep track of the advertisements for headache remedies.

"Which aspirin do doctors recommend most often?" asks an actor in a white coat.

"Product X is the best!" says one advertiser.

Others ask, "What tablets do hospitals use most?" or "Which one is best for your child?"

So much television time is given to headache medicine! Why are there fewer ads for drugs to treat more serious diseases, such as epilepsy or meningitis? It's simple. More people have headaches than have epilepsy or meningitis.

Medicine companies try to sell products that more people need. As you read this section, keep this in mind. Most of the ailments that are described here are uncommon ones.

Headaches

Almost everyone has had a headache at one time or another. Simple headaches can be treated with aspirin or other painkillers. Sometimes, bed rest or a dose of fresh air can help. Other times, just relaxing does the trick.

Getting a headache does not mean that there is something wrong with your brain. Most headaches have nothing to do with the brain. Headaches are usually caused by **tension**. Tension is strain or stress in your muscles or nerves.

A **migraine headache** is more painful than a regular headache. It often lasts longer, too. The pain is usually on one side of the head. Nausea or vomiting can accompany a migraine. Some people see flashing lights. Others cannot stand the slightest sound or movement. Sometimes, aspirin or other painkillers can help migraine sufferers. But some people need a doctor's help to deal with the pain. Doctors usually perform some tests to make sure there is no serious brain disorder. They can then prescribe drugs that are stronger than over-the-counter medicines. Doctors need to write a prescription for many kinds of drugs.

Epilepsy

Perhaps you have seen someone fall to the floor and violently shake. That person could be having a **convulsion**, or epileptic seizure. The disease that causes these convulsions is **epilepsy**. It is a disease in which the brain tissue is irritated. This irritation causes an electrical imbalance in the brain. This imbalance produces convulsions. Epilepsy can be caused by a brain injury or a chemical imbalance.

There are several forms of epilepsy. Most persons with epilepsy have one of two kinds of this disorder. In the mild type, a person might seem to be "out of it" for a few seconds. If the epilepsy is more serious, convulsions occur. Epilepsy can usually be controlled by certain medicines. With good medical care and appropriate medication taken just as prescribed, seizures can be controlled or eliminated.

Cerebral Palsy

Cerebral palsy results from damage to the central nervous system, either when a person is born or during early childhood. It is a disorder that affects certain muscles of the body. The muscles become tense, or contracted. This makes it difficult to walk or talk. There is no cure for cerebral palsy. Exercise, physical therapy, speech therapy, and special walking devices can sometimes help a person with cerebral palsy lead a more normal life.

Multiple Sclerosis

Multiple sclerosis is a nerve disease that strikes young adults. People are disabled in different ways, depending on which nerves are damaged by the disease. Some people have speech and hearing problems. Others get numb, or walk only with difficulty. At this time, there is no cure for multiple sclerosis, but some medications help to control some of the problems it causes.

Meningitis

Meningitis is also called spinal meningitis. It is an infection of the membranes that surround the brain and spinal cord. Meningitis is an infectious disease, just like the common cold. It is caused by **bacteria**. You can catch meningitis by close contact with someone who has the disease. It is spread by coughing, sneezing, or other forms of contact. Headache, fever, chills, a rash, and a stiff neck are some of the symptoms of this disease. Meningitis usually affects children and teenagers. A doctor can cure this disease by giving the patient **antibiotics**. These are drugs that fight the germs that cause a disease. This is one nervous system disease in which good medical care really makes a difference. If not treated, meningitis can cause paralysis and even death.

Stroke

A **stroke** generally affects older people. It happens when blood that usually goes to the brain is stopped by a blood clot. A blood clot is a clump of blood and other tissue that plugs up a blood vessel. Without blood, the brain cannot function.

Blood clots stop the blood from getting to certain parts of the brain. This stops these parts of the brain from functioning. The body part that the damaged section of brain controls is then paralyzed.

Sometimes, physical therapy can help another part of the brain take over the work of the damaged section. But, sometimes, the damage is permanent. Strokes can cause you to lose your ability to speak or use different parts of your body.

Medical research has shown that smoking and high blood pressure can increase your chances of having a stroke.

Alzheimer's Disease

Alzheimer's disease is an illness that usually strikes older people. It affects the brain, and the victim becomes very forgetful. **Senility** occurs in some people as they grow older. They lose their mental powers and memory and become confused.

CHECK YOUR UNDERSTANDING
1. What is the cause of most headaches?
2. Define epilepsy.
3. Name a nervous system disease that is infectious.
4. Name a nervous system disease that affects older people.
5. Why does a stroke damage only some body parts?

The eyes, ears, nose, tongue, and skin are sense organs that receive information.

Sense Organs

The eyes, ears, tongue, nose, and skin are your body's windows. Through these **sense organs**, you can find out many things about your environment.

The sense organs take in energy from the environment and change it into nerve impulses. The nerves carry these impulses to the brain. The brain translates the impulses into something you can understand. Impulses from the eyes are translated into pictures. Impulses from the ears become sounds. The windows of your body give you a beautiful view and a marvelous concert.

How the Eyes Work

Light energy from the objects you see enters the eye through the **cornea**. This is a transparent layer of matter that covers the eye. The cornea sends the light on through the eye to the **pupil**, which is the middle part of your eye that gets larger and smaller. The pupil lets in exactly the right amount of light. It gets smaller when you are in a bright, sunny place. This limits the amount of light that enters the eye. It gets larger when you are in a dark place, taking advantage of all the light that is available.

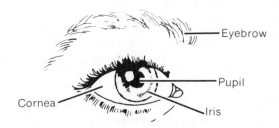

Eyebrow

Pupil

Cornea

Iris

Behind the pupil is a soft, clear tissue called the **lens**. It works just like the lens of a camera. It focuses the light energy onto the **retina**. The retina contains special **receptor cells** that send the light information on to the **optic nerve**. The optic nerve quickly sends this information on to the brain. The brain looks at the light impulses and translates them into pictures that you can understand. All of this happens very, very quickly.

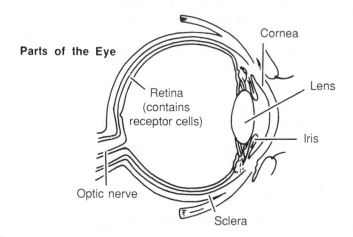

Parts of the Eye

Cornea

Lens

Retina (contains receptor cells)

Iris

Optic nerve

Sclera

How the Ears Work

You probably don't notice that the air vibrates when a sound is made, but your ears do. The outer ear sends the sound vibrations through your ear canal to the **eardrum**. The eardrum actually looks like a drum. It is a thin piece of tissue that is stretched across the ear canal. Once it receives the vibrations, the eardrum starts to vibrate, too. This causes three small bones in the middle ear to vibrate. The three bones are the hammer, anvil, and stirrup. They make the vibrations much louder. They pass the sound energy on to the inner ear. Receptor cells here transfer the vibrations to the **auditory nerve**. The auditory nerve passes its information on to the brain. The brain interprets the message. It tells the person what kind of a sound has occurred. All of this can happen in the time it takes for the sound to occur.

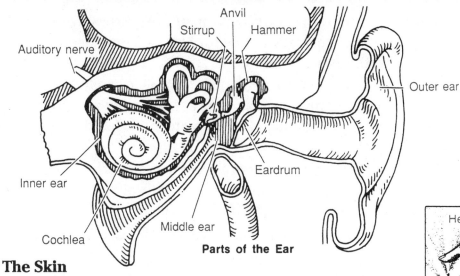

Anvil
Stirrup | Hammer
Auditory nerve
Outer ear
Inner ear
Cochlea
Middle ear
Eardrum

Parts of the Ear

The Skin

Most people do not think of the skin as a sense organ, but it is. In fact, the skin is the largest sense organ that the body has. All over the skin, **sense receptors** receive and process many different sensations. There are different receptors for touch, pressure, pain, heat, and cold. Your lips and fingertips are more sensitive than any other part of your body because they have more sense receptors.

What happens when you cut your hand with a knife? First, the pain receptors in your skin receive the sensation. The sensation travels through the nerves to the spinal column and the brain. The brain knows that you are in pain, even before you feel it. The nerves in the spinal cord send a message to the muscles, telling you to move your hand. This immediate reflex action protects you from further injury.

The Nose and Tongue

Your tongue and nose have much in common. Both contain receptor cells. These receptor cells help you tell, by using your nose, how a thing smells, and, by using your tongue, how a thing tastes.

The nerves in the nose are part of the olfactory nerve that connects to the brain. When your nose detects an

Heat

Cold

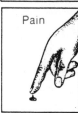
Pain

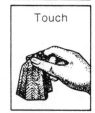
Touch

Pressure

odor, it transmits this information to the brain by sending a message over the olfactory nerve. Your nose can react to thousands of different smells.

The tongue can distinguish only four kinds of taste: sweet, sour, bitter, and salty. Taste buds which contain receptors for each kind of taste are located in different parts of the tongue.

Taste and smell are closely connected. When you chew your food, smells reach your olfactory nerve, so you are smelling the food, as well as tasting it.

CHECK YOUR UNDERSTANDING

1. Why do the pupils of your eyes get larger and smaller?
2. Describe what happens to sound vibration as it travels from the outer ear to the inner ear.
3. Explain how reflex actions keep you safe.
4. Match the sense organ with the sense.

   Eyes   a. Smell

   Ears   b. Taste

   Nose   c. Touch

   Tongue   d. Sight

   Skin   e. Hearing

5. Name the sensations that different skin receptors receive.

KEY IDEA #4:
Problems of the eyes and ears include varying degrees of blindness and hearing loss.

A Broken Window

In the last section, you learned that the senses are the windows of the body. Each window, in its own way, helps you to learn about your environment. Think how different the world would seem if one of these windows of the senses were damaged or broken.

Some people are born with disorders and diseases that affect their sense organs. But some disorders are the result of accidents that could have been prevented. Once a window is broken, it is not very hard to replace. Once you have permanently injured a sense organ like the eyes, you can't replace or fix it easily.

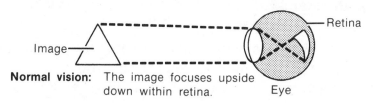

Normal vision: The image focuses upside down within retina.

Defects of Vision

For your eyes to produce a clear image, light rays must focus on the retina. If the eyeball is too long, the light focuses in front of the retina. The brain gets a distorted image that is hard for it to interpret. This condition is called **nearsightedness.** If you are nearsighted, you can see only objects that are near you. Objects that are far away look unclear or fuzzy.

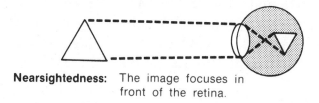

Nearsightedness: The image focuses in front of the retina.

On the other hand, if the eyeball is too short, light focuses in back of the retina. You have difficulty seeing objects that are close to you. You can see only distant objects clearly. This condition is called **farsightedness**.

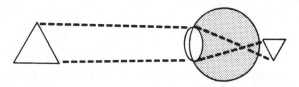

Farsightedness: The image focuses behind the retina.

Glasses and Contacts

Glasses or contact lenses can correct your vision if you are nearsighted or farsighted. An optometrist or ophthalmologist can examine your eyes and fit you for either glasses or contact lenses. An **optometrist** is a licensed technician or doctor of optometry. An **ophthalmologist** is a medical doctor who specializes in eye care.

Both the optometrist and ophthalmologist use an eye chart to test how well you can see from a distance. The chart usually has a big **E** at the top. The letters of each line get smaller and smaller as you read from the chart. If you can read the second line from the bottom (the 20 line) from 20 feet away, you have 20/20, or perfect, vision.

At one time, most people who had visual defects chose eyeglasses over contact lenses. Contact lenses were expensive and difficult to wear. The lenses could irritate eyes. They had to be taken out every night. Gradually, contact lenses were improved. Soft lenses were invented. People liked to wear the soft lenses because they were comfortable. They could also be worn for longer periods of time. Today, both contact lenses and glasses are quite common.

Strabismus

There are several muscles that control eye movement. When one of these muscles is weak, the eyeball is pulled in an abnormal way. This condition is called **strabismus**. The brain cannot use the images that come from the eyes because each eye gives it such a different picture. The brain will ignore the image from the weaker eye. Because it does not get as much use, the weak eye gets even weaker. Surgery, eye exercises, and glasses can improve this condition. A person who has strabismus should be treated as soon as the disorder is discovered, preferably before the age of two.

Eye Diseases of Older People

Glaucoma, cataracts, and a **detached retina** are three eye disorders that affect older people. In years past, a person with one of these conditions would surely go blind. Today, ophthalmologists can usually correct them with surgery.

If a person has glaucoma, the pressure in the eyeball changes. This makes the eyeball hard. Gradually, a person's vision is destroyed. This is such a common disease that many states require doctors to include a test for glaucoma in every eye exam they give to people over forty years of age.

A cataract is a clouding of the eye's lens. Slowly, the cataract grows, blocking more and more of a person's vision. This disease can be corrected before it causes blindness. A surgeon can remove the damaged lens and replace it with an artificial one.

Sometimes, the retina comes loose from the rest of the eye. Fluid collects under the detached part of the eye. This makes it impossible for the retina to interpret correctly the light rays coming through the lens. Retinal detachment is a medical emergency and requires immediate treatment to avoid permanent loss of vision. Surgery is the only effective treatment. A person with this condition will not be able to see until surgery repairs the damage.

Eye Injuries

Eye injuries can lead to partial or total blindness. Protecting your eyes can prevent accidental blindness. There are several steps that you can take to do this. Be careful when you use sharp objects or harsh chemicals, like bleach. Always wear safety goggles when you work with power tools or play games like racquetball. Science and shop labs in schools require the use of safety glasses. If you do injure your eyes, be sure to see a doctor immediately in order to prevent more damage from occurring.

If your cornea gets badly scarred by an accident or from a disease, it must be replaced, or you will be permanently blind. A **corneal transplant** is necessary. A fresh cornea is taken from an **eye donor.** These are people who have decided to donate their eyes to a medical institution when they die.

Eye Infections

An **infection** can cause the eyes to tear and burn. Touching the eyes with dirty hands only makes the situation worse. Two common eye infections are pinkeye and sties. **Pinkeye** causes the eyes to get wet and runny. It is extremely contagious. A **sty** sometimes forms on the eyelid. It looks like a pimple and is caused by bacteria.

Blindness

People who are blind or partially blind can use other senses and objects to help compensate for their loss of sight. They can read books and magazines that are written in braille. Braille is a kind of writing that uses raised dots to stand for letters. Blind people move their fingertips over the braille writing in order to read. Some blind people use seeing-eye dogs to help them. Others use canes. Blind people tap a cane on the ground while walking. By listening to the sound the cane makes, they are able to recognize the territory in front of them.

Causes of Deafness

An estimated twenty-five million people in the United States have some kind of hearing loss. One cause of deafness can start as an infection in the middle ear. If an infection is not treated, pressure may build up around the eardrum, causing it to burst. The infection can spread to the bones behind the eardrum, and growths called adhesions may form. These complications can be prevented if ear infections are treated by a doctor. The antibiotics that are prescribed will destroy bacterial infections.

Otosclerosis is a disease in which growth of spongy bone occurs at the entrance of the inner ear. People with this condition can have varying degrees of hearing loss.

Otosclerosis causes a change in the bones. This change closes the oval window, fusing the stirrup bone to the window. It is estimated that ten percent of the American population has some degree of otosclerosis.

Constant noise and loud music can also cause deafness. This is why many musicians wear earplugs. They want to protect their hearing. Occasional loud noise or music probably will not hurt your ears, but a constant battering of very loud sounds will.

German Measles

German measles, or rubella, is a mild form of the measles. Sometimes people are not even aware that they have it. However, this disease can be serious. If a woman gets German measles during the early stages of pregnancy, her baby could be born totally deaf.

During childhood, most people are vaccinated to prevent them from getting German measles. If a woman has not been vaccinated and is thinking about having a family, she should be vaccinated at least three months before she gets pregnant. The vaccine is so powerful that it too can cause deafness in the unborn child.

Hearing Aids

A **hearing aid** can be helpful to a person whose ear is damaged or not working properly. Hearing aids work in one of two ways. They can make sounds louder, or they can carry sounds toward the inner ear.

Educating the Deaf

Deaf people can learn to communicate by **signing** with their hands. In sign language, the hands, along with appropriate facial expressions, are used to make symbols for words and phrases. Deaf people also use finger spelling. This method of communicating gives a certain finger position to each letter of the alphabet. It is a much slower way of communicating.

However, deaf people can use these two systems

only with people who understand them. That is why some deaf people learn to read lips. This is a very difficult process, because so many sounds look alike when we say them. One method that combines lip reading with finger spelling seems to be a solution to this problem. It is called cued speech.

There are special schools and programs for the deaf to help them learn to communicate. For example, the major television networks now caption some television programs. Deaf people can purchase special machines that attach to their televisions. These machines read the captions, or words that are being said, onto the screen. Deaf persons can then "hear" what is being said by reading.

Care of the Ear

You probably were told to wash your ears when you were a child. Cleaning your ears with soap and a washcloth is fine. But you should never put small devices, like cotton swabs, in your ear.

It is normal for your ears to have some wax in them. The wax is a coating that protects your ears. In some cases, the wax may get too thick. If this happens, it should be removed. Only a trained health professional should do this.

CHECK YOUR UNDERSTANDING

1. Which activity might be more difficult for a near-sighted person who has lost his glasses—reading the blackboard while sitting in the back of the classroom, or reading a book that is on his desk?
2. Tell the difference between an optometrist and an ophthalmologist.
3. What are cataracts? How can doctors correct this condition?
4. Name two causes of deafness.
5. What does a hearing aid do?

Summary of Chapter 3

The brain, spinal cord, and peripheral nerves make up the body's nervous system. The cerebrum, cerebellum, and brain stem are the main parts of the brain. The cerebrum controls thinking, and the cerebellum controls coordination. The medulla, located in the brain stem, controls the body's automatic activities. The spinal nerves and the peripheral nerves transmit information to and from the brain, the body, and the outside world. The autonomic nervous system regulates the body's automatic actions. Reflexes are automatic actions.

Headaches are the most common disorder of the nervous system. Other nervous system disorders are epilepsy, cerebral palsy, multiple sclerosis, meningitis, stroke, and Alzheimer's disease. Some of these conditions can be controlled with medicine or physical therapy.

The eyes, ears, nose, tongue, and skin are sense organs that gather information from the environment. The cornea, pupil, lens, and retina are parts of the eye. The optic nerves send the information they get from the retina to the brain. The brain signals what you are seeing.

Vibrations travel from the outer ear to the middle ear, where the eardrum vibrates and the small bones behind it make the sound louder. The vibrations then reach the inner ear, the auditory nerve, and the brain, where they are translated into sounds.

The skin has receptors for touch, pressure, pain, heat, and cold. Receptors for taste are called taste buds.

Nearsightedness is the inability to see from a distance. Farsightedness is the inability to see close up. Glasses and contact lenses can correct these defects. Eye diseases of older people, such as glaucoma, a detached retina, and cataracts, can also be treated. Middle ear infections, otosclerosis, and German measles are causes of deafness.

WORDS TO USE

1. brain
2. spinal cord
3. peripheral nerves
4. cerebrum
5. cerebellum
6. brain stem
7. medulla
8. automatic activities
9. paralysis
10. central nervous system
11. autonomic nervous system
12. reflexes
13. tension
14. migraine headache
15. epilepsy
16. convulsion
17. cerebral palsy
18. multiple sclerosis
19. meningitis
20. bacteria
21. antibiotics
22. stroke
23. Alzheimer's disease
24. senility
25. sense organs
26. cornea
27. pupil
28. lens
29. retina
30. receptor cells
31. optic nerve
32. eardrum
33. auditory nerve
34. sense receptor
35. nearsightedness
36. farsightedness
37. optometrist
38. ophthalmologist
39. strabismus
40. glaucoma
41. cataracts
42. detached retina
43. corneal transplant
44. eye donor
45. infection
46. pinkeye
47. otosclerosis
48. German measles
49. hearing aid
50. signing, sign language
51. sty

REVIEW QUESTIONS FOR CHAPTER 3

1. Name the part of the brain that enables you to think and remember.

2. What part of the brain controls automatic body functions?

3. Where is the spinal cord located?

4. Name three parts of the nervous system.

5. How is a migraine different from an ordinary headache?

6. What disease causes people to have convulsions or seizures?

7. List the symptoms of multiple sclerosis.

8. What is Alzheimer's disease?

9. Where is the retina, and what happens there?

10. What is the optic nerve?

11. Where is the olfactory nerve located?

12. Name the four kinds of taste your tongue can distinguish.

13. Describe farsightedness.

14. What does 20/20 vision mean?

15. Name two advantages that soft contact lenses have over hard contact lenses.

16. What is a corneal transplant?

17. List two common infections of the eye.

18. Why should women be vaccinated against German measles?

19. List two things you can do to prevent damage to your ear.

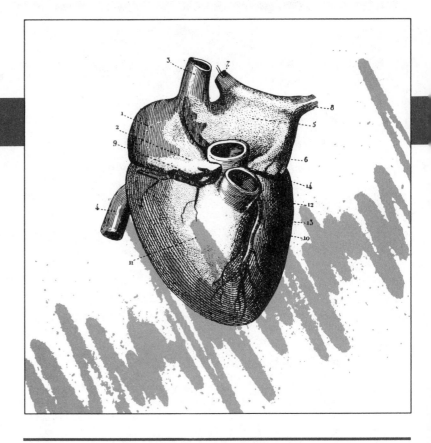

CHAPTER GOALS:

To know how your body works so that you can help to keep it in good health.

To describe the circulatory system as a transport system for oxygen, food, and cell wastes.

To know about diseases of the cardiovascular system.

KEY IDEAS:

The blood, the heart, and the blood vessels work together as a blood transport system.

Blood is a special fluid that helps keep the body healthy.

The heart is a double pump that powers the blood transport system.

The circulatory system has a network of blood vessels that includes arteries, capillaries, and veins.

Diseases of the cardiovascular system are a leading cause of death.

CHAPTER 4

The Circulatory System

KEY IDEA #1:
The blood, the heart, and the blood vessels work together as a blood transport system.

Circulatory Transport System

Your **circulatory system** is a well-designed transport system. A transport system carries things from one place to the other. Your circulatory system is made up of blood, the heart, and three kinds of blood vessels. These blood vessels are called arteries, veins, and capillaries. Every body system has a structure, or parts, that interact with each other. Every system has a **function,** or job, to carry out.

A Natural System

The circulatory system is a natural system that transports blood through the body. Blood is the workhorse of the system because it carries oxygen and food to every cell in the body. Cells need the food and the oxygen to do their work. As the cells do their special jobs, carbon dioxide and other waste products are formed. The blood carries these wastes away from the cells.

The circulatory system also regulates body temperatures. It helps cool us off when we are hot. In cold conditions, it helps keep us warm.

Another important job this system does is to carry substances that help to prevent disease.

A Human-Made System

An example of a human-made system is a metro rail system. It has trains, tracks, and stations. Each of these basic parts is made up of many other things. For example, the metro stations have entrances, exits, escalators, fare machines, loading platforms, and control centers. All of these parts are designed to get passengers to their destinations. This does not happen by chance. The people who control the metro system set up a regular schedule for trains. Then they make sure the trains follow that schedule.

The key to operating the metro system safely and on schedule is care and maintenance. The cars must be repaired and maintained. The tracks must be kept in good condition, too. Knowing what needs to be done is just as important as doing it.

This is also true with body systems, including the circulatory system. You need to know about the structure and function of the system to help keep it healthy. You cannot wait until the whole system breaks down. You must take **preventive** health measures to keep the system going. Preventing problems ensures a healthy circulatory system. Keep in mind the old saying, "An ounce of prevention is worth a pound of cure."

1. In what way is the circulatory system a transport system?

2. Give an example of a human-made system.

3. List similarities between a natural transportation system and a human-made system.

4. Why is it important to prevent systems from breaking down?

KEY IDEA #2:

Blood is a special fluid that helps keep the body healthy.

Blood—The Workhorse

Blood is called a fluid tissue. Tissues are groups of body cells that work together to do a certain job. Blood is made up of **plasma**, **red blood cells**, **white blood cells**, and **platelets**. The cells and the platelets are suspended in the plasma. Each part of the blood has a specific job.

Red Blood Cells and Oxygen

Red blood cells are shaped like discs. Their centers are pushed in, or indented. The shape is important because it gives red blood cells a large surface area. This larger surface area allows room for greater chemical exchange.

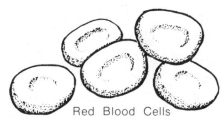
Red Blood Cells

The main job of the red blood cells is to carry oxygen to all parts of the body and to remove carbon dioxide from those body parts. A special substance called **hemoglobin** allows these cells to do this.

Hemoglobin's first job is to attract and hold oxygen. It meets oxygen in the small blood vessels in your lungs. The oxygen comes from the air you breathe. As blood travels through the lungs, hemoglobin pulls oxygen into the red blood cells. When the blood reaches a muscle or organ, hemoglobin releases just the right amount of oxygen for that body part. Then the hemoglobin is ready to do its second job. It picks up any carbon dioxide that needs to be removed and carries this waste back to the lungs, where it is breathed out. Hemoglobin is also the substance that makes your blood red.

Red blood cells are manufactured in the soft centers, or **marrow,** of long bones. Red blood cells last about 120 days. Then they must be replaced. Old red blood cells are destroyed in the **spleen** and the **liver**. New red blood cells enter the bloodstream from the bone marrow. This is one way that a healthy circulation system maintains itself.

White Blood Cells and Infection

White blood cells defend your body against infection and disease. When your body is invaded by infection-causing bacteria, the number of white blood cells increases. The white blood cells surround the bacteria and "eat" it up. White blood cells also produce other substances called **antibodies**. Antibodies fight invading viruses and infectious diseases. This is an example of how the body has its own built-in system of protection and maintenance.

A white blood cell eating bacteria.

Basic Health

White blood cells are also made in the bone marrow. They have the ability to change their shape and move from the blood vessels into body cells.

A white blood cell moves like an inchworm.

Platelets are the smallest element in the blood. They help the blood coagulate, or clot, at the site of a cut. Platelets seal off the wound temporarily. They also release chemicals that react with other chemicals in the plasma to form a clot. This stops the bleeding.

Plasma

Most of your blood is made up of plasma. Plasma itself is 90 percent water. It also contains proteins, salts, nutrients, and waste products. The proteins control the amount of water in the plasma, carry antibodies to protect against disease, and help the blood to clot.

CHECK YOUR UNDERSTANDING
1. Define tissues.
2. What is the main job of the red blood cells?
3. Describe hemoglobin.
4. Where are red and white blood cells formed?
5. When you have an infection, what happens to the white blood cells?
6. How do platelets help stop bleeding?
7. What is plasma?
8. List three jobs that the protein in plasma does.

Your Heart

Your heart is a marvelous power machine. Its size varies, but it is usually the size of an adult's fist and weighs about a pound. It is located between your lungs in the middle of your chest. Without the heart's work, your body could not survive.

A Double Pump

Your heart is a muscular double set of pumps that is divided into a right side and a left side. The right pump pushes blood to the lungs. The left pump pushes blood to all other parts of the body.

You already know that blood has many special tasks to do. In order for it to do that work, it has to move around the body. Blood can't do that by itself, the heart has to move it.

The Heart's Job

Blood from all parts of the body flows into the part, or chamber, of the heart called the **right atrium**. This blood comes into the chamber through two big veins. They are called the **inferior vena cava** and the **superior vena cava**. This blood is full of carbon dioxide, which it needs to get rid of. The blood also needs to pick up oxygen.

The right atrium contracts and pushes the blood into the lower right part of the heart that is below it. This part is called the **right ventricle**. The right ventricle contracts, forcing the blood to the lungs. The blood travels to the lungs through passageways called the **pulmonary arteries**.

In the lungs, the blood releases carbon dioxide and picks up oxygen. The blood is now **oxygenated.** It has oxygen in it. The first part of the heart's job is now complete.

The oxygenated blood travels back to the heart through the **pulmonary veins.** It goes into the left atrium on the left side of the heart to start the second part of its job.

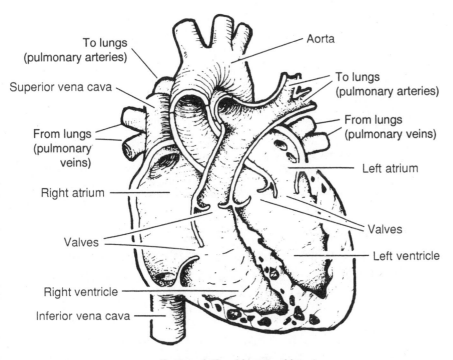

To lungs (pulmonary arteries)

Aorta

Superior vena cava

To lungs (pulmonary arteries)

From lungs (pulmonary veins)

From lungs (pulmonary veins)

Left atrium

Right atrium

Valves

Valves

Left ventricle

Right ventricle

Inferior vena cava

Parts of the Human Heart

The oxygenated blood collects in the **left atrium.** The left atrium pushes the blood into the **left ventricle.** The left ventricle is the most powerful pump of the heart. It pushes the blood to all parts of the body. The heart itself gets a supply of blood from the left ventricle.

The main blood vessel that carries oxygenated blood to the body is called the **aorta.** Some branches of the aorta go to the head and brain, to the neck and arms, and to the heart itself. The main branch of the aorta turns and goes down to the body, trunk, and legs. Other branches go to the body's main organs.

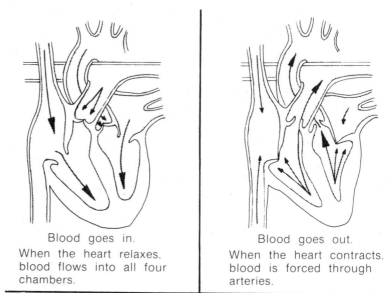

| Blood goes in. When the heart relaxes, blood flows into all four chambers. | Blood goes out. When the heart contracts, blood is forced through arteries. |

Your Heartbeat

The regular beating of a healthy heart is rhythmic. The heart muscle repeatedly contracts and relaxes. Each of the four parts of the heart does its job just like clockwork.

The right atrium and the left atrium contract at the same time. The larger and more muscular right ventricle and left ventricle also contract at the same time. There is a **valve** that separates the right atrium from the right ventricle. A valve also separates the left atrium from the left ventricle. These valves control the flow of blood between these parts, or chambers, of the heart. They open and close in time to a rhythmic beat. Your heartbeat actually is the sound of your heart valves opening and closing.

The doctor uses a stethoscope to listen to these sounds. A stethoscope is a flat disc with two rubber tubes. The doctor puts the tubes in his ears to listen to the heartbeat. He is trained to hear any irregularities. Sometimes, slight malfunctions of the valves, called **heart murmurs**, are discovered this way. Many heart murmurs are normal.

Your Heart Rate

Each person has a different heart rate. The average rate is about 72 beats per minute when the body is resting. When you exercise, your body needs more oxygen and more nutrients. Your heart responds to this by speeding up its work.

CHECK YOUR UNDERSTANDING

1. Describe the heart's main job.
2. Name the four parts, or chambers, of the heart.
3. Which blood vessels empty blood from the body into the right atrium?
4. Name the arteries that carry blood from the heart to the lungs.
5. What is oxygenated blood?
6. Describe what the aorta does.
7. What makes the sounds that we call our heartbeat?
8. What instrument allows a doctor to listen to heartbeats?
9. Describe heart murmurs.

KEY IDEA #4:
The circulatory system has a network of blood vessels
that includes arteries, capillaries, and veins.

Blood Vessels

Blood vessels are routes that blood takes to get to all parts of the body. The circulatory system has a remarkably intricate network of blood vessels. These include **arteries**, **capillaries**, and **veins**.

Arteries

Arteries have thick walls. Blood from the heart is forced through these strong, muscular tubes. The main artery from the heart carries oxygenated blood. It is called the aorta. Two branches of the aorta, called **coronary arteries**, bring blood to the heart itself. Other branches of the aorta go to other parts of the body and its main organs. The branches of the aorta divide into smaller and smaller arteries as the blood travels away from the heart. The smallest artery is called an **arteriole**.

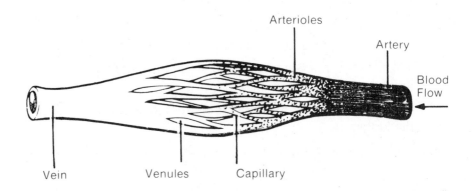

Types of Blood Vessels

Capillaries

Blood from the arterioles flows into the capillaries. The capillaries are the smallest blood vessels in the body. They also have the thinnest walls. These thin walls allow nutrients and oxygen to pass out of the bloodstream and into the cells. Waste products, dissolved in the body fluids, can also pass through these walls from the cells to the blood. Now, the blood begins its return trip to the heart.

Veins

Blood leaves the capillaries and enters the smallest veins in the body. These veins are called **venules**. Gradually, these veins become larger and larger, until two major veins bring the "used" blood back to the heart. These major veins are the inferior vena cava and the superior vena cava.

Veins have thinner walls than arteries do. Veins have one-way valves inside them. These valves control the blood flow toward the heart. There is no separate pumping system for the veins. The movement of the surrounding muscles keeps the blood flowing back toward the heart. The closing valves do not allow blood to flow backwards.

This system of vessels that carry blood is a closed, one-way system. Blood flows at a fast pace. It makes one trip through this entire body system in about a minute.

CHECK YOUR UNDERSTANDING

1. List the three kinds of blood vessels that make up the circulatory system.
2. Name two main arteries that carry oxygenated blood from the heart.
3. Define an arteriole.
4. Describe the role of capillaries with thin walls.
5. What is a venule?

Cardiovascular Diseases

The leading cause of death in the United States is heart disease. The heart is the major organ in the **cardiovascular system**. The prefix cardio- means "heart." Vascular means "relating to the blood vessels." Your heart and blood vessels are affected by your life-style.

What are some things that are part of your life-style? Your diet, the amount and kind of exercise that you get, your body weight, your blood pressure, and your smoking and drinking habits are major parts of your life-style. They play a big role in determining the condition of your heart and blood vessels. **Cardiovascular disease** is most often related to one or more of the life-style factors mentioned.

Older people are victims of heart and vascular disease more often than younger people. But their disease started when they were younger. That is why it is so important for you to practice a healthful life-style in your early years.

Good Health Measures

Exercise is an important part of a healthful life-style. Regular exercise does several things. First, it helps strengthen the heart muscles. This helps blood circulation. In addition, regular exercise helps promote normal blood pressure in the arteries. Exercise such as walking and running can be a habit that is a regular part of your life-style. Research has shown that these kinds of exercise help prevent cardiovascular disease.

Maintaining a good diet is another good health practice. Diet goes hand in hand with exercise to prevent heart and vascular diseases.

Tied closely with the other good health measures is the decision not to smoke cigarettes. The surgeon general of the United States has warned the public about the dangers of smoking. Smoking has been named as a factor in causing heart disease, as well as cancer. Television viewers have been given the message: "If you don't smoke, don't start! If you do smoke, quit!" Cigarette advertisements in magazines must contain statements like this one:

Surgeon General's Warning:
Quitting Smoking Now Greatly Reduces
Serious Risks To Your Health.

High Blood Pressure

During a routine physical examination, a doctor usually checks the patient's **blood pressure**. Blood pressure is the force the blood exerts on the walls of the arteries. This force is greater when the heart is contracting than when it is relaxing. The doctor needs to know the pressure at both of these times. When the heart muscle contracts, the doctor measures the **systolic pressure**. Then he takes a reading when the heart is relaxing. This is called the **diastolic pressure**. He uses an instrument called a **sphygmomanometer.**

Blood pressure readings vary according to what a person is doing or how that person is feeling. A normal reading is 120/80. The first number is the systolic pressure reading. The second is the diastolic reading.

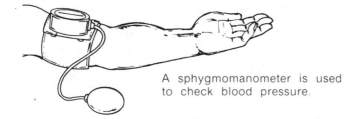

A sphygmomanometer is used to check blood pressure.

If a person's blood pressure is consistently above 140/90, it is considered to be high. High blood pressure, or **hypertension**, should be treated by a doctor. Usually, a doctor uses a combination of methods to treat hypertension. Some of these methods might include a change of diet, an exercise program, and prescription medicines.

No one knows exactly what causes high blood pressure. There are some factors that are linked with it. These include being overweight, having a family history of heart trouble, and having excess emotional tension or stress. Too much salt in your diet might be another cause.

Rheumatic Heart Disease

Sometimes a **streptococcus** throat infection can lead to a condition called **rheumatic fever.** This infection, which most people call strep throat, has to be treated by a doctor. If it is not, the bacteria that cause this disease may affect your heart valves. It will make it harder for them to open and close. This condition is called rheumatic fever. As a result of this, the heart has to work harder. This causes fatigue, shortness of breath, and chest pains.

It is fairly easy to prevent this disease. A person who has a sore throat, fever, nausea, and swollen joints or glands needs to see a doctor at once. The person should immediately take the antibiotic that the doctor prescribes. The antibiotic will fight the infection. Today, rheumatic fever is less common, because most people who have strep throat get the treatment they need.

Disease in the Arteries and Arterioles

Atherosclerosis is a life-threatening disease of the arteries. It happens when the walls of the arteries become thick. When you are born, your artery walls are smooth. But, as you get older, calcium and fat start sticking to the walls. These deposits cause the artery walls to break down. As the cells break down, they irritate other cells nearby. The nearby cells form scars. The deposits and the scars build up and make the artery narrower. The heart has to work much harder to push the blood through. If this condition continues, it can lead to many dangerous conditions. It can even cause the heart to stop working. If you want to keep this from

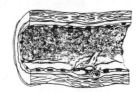

Cholesterol begins to build up on the wall of the artery.

The fatty patch grows.

The artery becomes narrow and blocks the flow of blood.

happening, you have to pay attention to the foods you eat. The best diet is one that provides a variety of nutrients, but is low in animal fats, or **cholesterol**, and low in salt and sugar. Maintaining a normal body weight through these methods contributes greatly to the good health of your cardiovascular system.

Heart Attacks

Coronary arteries supply oxygenated blood to the heart. If fat and calcium deposits make these arteries hard and narrow, the heart may not get enough blood. Without enough blood, the heart cannot get enough of the oxygen the blood carries. When the oxygen supply gets too low, it causes cells in the heart to die. If enough of these cells die, the heart stops working. This is called a **heart attack**. A heart attack is a brief, sudden occurrence of **coronary disease**. A person suffering from a heart attack has strong chest pains.

Atherosclerosis, or clogging and narrowing of the arteries, is the main cause of coronary disease.

Coronary disease may also occur as the result of a blood clot. A blood clot may block a coronary artery and cut off the blood and oxygen supply to the heart muscles. The heart may die for lack of blood.

Angina Pectoris

Some people do not have heart attacks, even though their coronary arteries are partly closed. They do have chest pain, though. It usually happens when they exercise or are under stress. This condition is known as **angina pectoris**. The pain is caused by a lack of oxygen in the heart muscles.

Angina pain can be controlled by rest and medicine. But it is a warning that a person's cardiovascular system is not well. Sometimes, doctors recommend bypass surgery to help this condition. In a bypass operation, the doctor constructs a detour around the blocked parts of the artery. Sections of clear arteries from the legs may be used to do this. Some people have more than one blocked artery. The doctor then has to perform more than one bypass at the same time.

Life-style and Heart Disease

Increased heart disease in the United States has been linked with certain life-styles. People who smoke have a greater chance of getting heart disease than those who do not smoke. Those who are overweight, have untreated high blood pressure, or have a high blood sugar level due to diabetes are also at greater risk of getting heart disease. An inactive life-style can also contribute to these problems.

Heart disease often occurs in older people. But it does not happen overnight. Right now, the life-style you have chosen could be leading to heart disease. By studying about health, you can make many important decisions about things that will affect you later on. This information can also help you guide your family and friends toward choosing a life-style that will keep them well.

CHECK YOUR UNDERSTANDING

1. What is the leading cause of death in the United States?

2. Define the term *cardiovascular*.

3. What does the surgeon general recommend about smoking?

4. Describe blood pressure.

5. What is rheumatic fever?

6. What causes atherosclerosis?

7. Describe the role of animal fats, or cholesterol, in arterial disease.

8. How does a heart attack occur?

9. What is the main cause of coronary disease?

10. List several reasons why teenagers should study about health.

Summary of Chapter 4

The circulatory system is a transport system. Its two most important jobs are bringing oxygenated blood to the cells and carrying away their waste products, including carbon dioxide. Having a healthy blood transport system requires good maintenance measures.

Blood is considered to be a tissue because it is a group of cells doing a certain job. This fluid tissue is made of plasma, white blood cells, red blood cells, and platelets.

The red blood cells carry oxygen. They do this with the help of hemoglobin. Hemoglobin can attract and hold oxygen. Red blood cells are manufactured in the bone marrow. Old red blood cells are destroyed in the spleen and liver.

White blood cells are useful in defending the body against infections and disease.

More than half the blood is made up of a fluid called plasma. This fluid carries salts, nutrients, waste products, and proteins.

The heart is a muscular, four-chambered pump. Blood carrying oxygen flows into the heart from the lungs. It is sent to all parts of the body. After the blood distributes the oxygen and picks up waste, it returns to the heart. The heart sends the blood back to the lungs to get rid of the waste, or carbon dioxide, and pick up more oxygen.

The heartbeat is rhythmic. Normally, the heart beats at a rate of about 72 beats per minute. It speeds up during exercise. The flow of blood through the heart is regulated by sets of valves. Your heartbeat is actually the sound of the valves opening and closing.

Arteries, veins, and capillaries are the three kinds of blood vessels in the circulatory system. Arteries carry blood away from the heart. Veins carry the blood back to the heart. Capillaries connect the two. Capillaries have very thin walls where oxygen leaves the blood. Wastes come back into the blood through the capillaries.

Diseases of the cardiovascular system are the leading cause of death in the United States. American life-styles contribute to the amount of heart and vascular disease. Measures can be taken to prevent such diseases. Smoking habits, diet, and exercise are factors that affect the health of the circulatory system.

High blood pressure, or hypertension, is an unhealthy condition that should be treated by a doctor. It can be controlled by exercise, diet, and medicine. Rheumatic heart disease can result from untreated strep throat. Atherosclerosis is a disease of the arteries that causes clogging and narrowing of the arteries. Cholesterol, or animal fats, and calcium deposits can build up in the blood vessels. A diet low in animal fats can help control this buildup.

The heart has its own set of arteries, called the coronary arteries. Coronary arteries can be affected by improper diet and lack of exercise. This can lead to a heart attack. Lack of oxygen to the heart muscles causes the chest pain that characterizes angina pectoris. This pain can be controlled by rest and medicine. It can sometimes be helped with bypass surgery.

WORDS TO USE

1. circulatory system
2. function
3. preventive
4. blood
5. plasma
6. red blood cells
7. white blood cells
8. platelets
9. hemoglobin
10. marrow
11. spleen
12. liver
13. antibodies
14. right atrium
15. inferior vena cava
16. superior vena cava
17. right ventricle
18. pulmonary arteries
19. oxygenated
20. pulmonary veins
21. left atrium
22. left ventricle
23. aorta
24. valve
25. heart murmurs
26. arteries
27. capillaries
28. veins
29. coronary arteries
30. arteriole
31. venule
32. cardiovascular system
33. cardiovascular disease
34. blood pressure
35. systolic pressure
36. sphygmomanometer
37. diastolic pressure
38. hypertension
39. streptococcus
40. rheumatic fever
41. atherosclerosis
42. cholesterol
43. heart attack
44. coronary disease
45. angina pectoris

1. What makes the circulatory system a transport system?

2. How does the circulatory system compare to a metro rail system?

3. What does "An ounce of prevention is worth a pound of cure" mean?

4. Why is blood considered a tissue?

5. What is the substance in the red blood cells that attracts and holds oxygen?

6. What makes the blood appear to be red?

7. Where are red blood cells manufactured?

8. Where does the destruction of red blood cells take place?

9. What do white blood cells do?

10. Give the name of the fluid part of the blood.

11. List substances found in the plasma.

12. Why can the heart be called a double pump?

13. What do the superior and inferior vena cava do?

14. Where does the blood go when it leaves the right ventricle?

15. What is oxygenated blood?

16. What do the valves in the heart do?

17. What exactly does the doctor hear when he or she listens to your heartbeat?

18. Describe heart murmurs.

19. Name the three kinds of blood vessels in the circulatory system.

20. What do capillaries do?

21. Give the meaning of the term *cardiovascular*.

22. What is another name for high blood pressure?

23. Tell the difference between systolic pressure and diastolic pressure.

24. What causes a heart attack?

25. List the causes of angina pectoris.

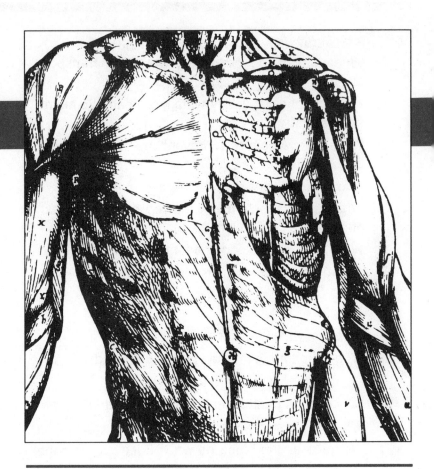

CHAPTER GOALS:

To describe the structure and function of the skeletal and muscular systems.

To recognize that the skeletal and muscular systems work together to make the body move.

KEY IDEAS:

The skeletal system supports the body, gives it shape, and protects the major organs. The bone marrow produces red and white blood cells.

The 206 bones in the human body have a variety of shapes that are suited to different jobs.

A joint is the meeting place for two bones. Joints allow the body to bend and move.

Muscles are responsible for movement of the body and for certain activities within the body.

CHAPTER 5

The Skeletal and Muscular Systems

KEY IDEA #1:
The skeletal system supports the body, gives it shape, and protects the major organs. The bone marrow produces red and white blood cells.

Your Skeleton

Imagine that you are a puppet without any strings. That is what you would be like without any **bones** and **muscles**. You would collapse to the ground. You would stay there, too, because you would not be able to move. Without bones and muscles, moving your body would not be possible.

Fortunately, you have bones and muscles to help you stand up straight; to give you shape; and to move your arms, legs, hands, and feet. In addition, your bones protect your internal organs from injury. Some bones also produce red and white blood cells from within.

Support, Shape, and Protection

The system of connected bones is called the **skeletal system**, or the skeleton. The skeletal system supports your body. Your skeleton keeps you upright, just as poles keep a canvas tent from collapsing.

Poles also give the tent its shape, so that it looks like a tent. Skeletons act like tent poles to give an elephant, a camel, or a human the shape that is distinctly theirs. Your legs, hips, head, and other body parts have certain shapes because of the way the underlying bones are shaped. Together, all your bones give your body a human shape.

Your skeleton also protects your organs. Put your hands on your chest. Do you feel the thin bones running across your chest? Those are your **ribs**. They form the rib cage that protects your heart and lungs. In the same way, the bones of your **cranium**, or skull, protect the brain from injury. Your eyes are also protected. They rest in bony sockets, or openings, in the skull.

What Bones Are Made Of

Bones are living material. Like all living things, they are made of **cells**. Cells are the basic structure of life. There are trillions of cells in your body. Each one of them has a specific job. There are blood cells, nerve cells, muscle cells, and bone cells. The same kind of cells doing the same kind of job form **tissues**. Muscle cells make up muscle tissue, and bone cells make up bone tissue.

Milk

Cheese

Spinach

Broccoli

Dairy products and some vegetables provide calcium.

Bones contain minerals, mainly **calcium**. Calcium is used in bone formation. It is important to get enough calcium from the foods you eat in order to keep your bones strong. You can get calcium by drinking milk and eating other dairy products and certain vegetables.

What Is Inside Bones

Your bones are strong enough to support your body. Yet they are very light. In fact, bones make up less than twenty percent of a person's weight. If you weighed 100 pounds, your bones would weigh less than twenty pounds. Bones are light because they are hollow.

The hollow center of a bone is filled with a special substance called **marrow**. Bone marrow makes both red and white blood cells. Blood cells become worn out or damaged. Then, they are destroyed. The marrow inside the long bones is like a factory. It constantly makes replacement blood cells.

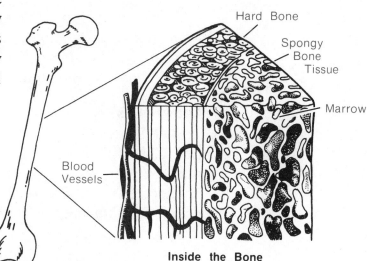

Inside the Bone

CHECK YOUR UNDERSTANDING

1. List three things your bones do for you.
2. How do milk and other dairy products help your bones?
3. What makes bones so light?
4. Tell where marrow is found and what it does.

The 206 bones in the human body have a variety of
shapes that are suited to different jobs.

Shape and Function

The bones of the body are a mixture of big and small
bones, flat and round bones, long and short bones,
narrow and wide bones, and specially-shaped bones.
This variety of shapes allows the body to do many
different things. The long bones of the legs allow the
body to stand up straight. The small bones in your back
allow you to bend and twist your body. Your bones are
shaped and positioned so that you can walk or run, twist
or turn, and sit or lie down.

Look at the diagram of the skeletal system in
Appendix A at the end of the book as you read this
section. It will help you become familiar with some of
the 206 bones in the human body.

Long Bones

The **femur**, or thigh bone, is the longest bone in the
body. The upper part of the femur is connected to the
hip bone, or **pelvis**. The lower part of the femur is
connected to the two lower leg bones. These bones are
called the **tibia** and the **fibula**.

Your arm is constructed somewhat like your leg. The
lower arm has two bones. They are called the **radius** and
ulna. A longer bone is located in the upper arm. It is
called the **humerus**. There is a humorous way to
remember the name of this bone. The humerus when
bumped sometimes gets a tingling or funny sensation at
the elbow. Thus, it is sometimes called the funny bone.

The Vertebrae

The **vertebrae** are the small bones that surround
your **spinal cord**. Each small bone in this system is

called a vertebra. The plural of vertebra is vertebrae. Another name for all the vertebrae is the **spinal column**, or **backbone**. Vertebrae protect the spinal cord, which is made up of nerves. This is an extremely important job. Injuries to the spinal cord can cause a loss of feeling in parts of your body. Victims of spinal cord injuries can even become paralyzed.

Despite this bony protection, the spinal cord can sometimes be injured. For example, people sometimes dive into an unfamiliar pool or lake. The water may turn out to be very shallow. The body's impact as it hits the bottom can seriously damage the diver's spine. Your body does have built-in protection systems. But your decisions can defeat even these systems.

The shape and construction of the vertebrae allow you to bend your back. Each vertebra is a small, round bone with a hole in it. The bones are stacked on top of each other. The spinal cord runs through the holes in the vertebrae.

An Experiment

Get some string and two drinking straws. Cut one of the straws into small pieces. Thread the string through the straw pieces. The string represents the spinal cord. The straw pieces are like vertebrae. You can easily move this "spinal column" because the vertebrae are small enough to allow it to bend.

There are 33 bones in the spinal column.

Each vertebra protects the spinal cord.

Now, take off the small pieces of straw. Put the thread through the whole drinking straw. Try to move the string. This is how inflexible you would be if you had only one vertebra to support your spinal cord.

Other Bones

The ribs form a cage that protects important organs. Ribs are thin bones. Some of them are attached in the front to a bone called the **sternum,** or breastbone. They protect your heart and lungs. The ribs also help you to breathe.

The cranium, or skull, protects the brain. Although the skull is very hard, it still can be injured by a sharp blow. This is why many people wear helmets when they play contact sports like football, or ride a motorcycle or bicycle.

Feel your jaw. It is made up of two bones. The upper jaw is fixed. It does not move. Only the lower jaw can move. Feel the place where the two bones are connected. It is on the side of your face by your ear.

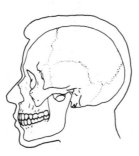
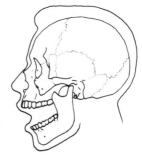

The upper jaw is fixed.

The lower jaw moves.

Basic Health

Broken Bones

Bones in the arms and the legs are the ones that are broken most often. When you break a bone, it is called a **fracture.** A fracture should be treated by a doctor. Usually the doctor moves the fractured bones together and puts a cast on the part of the body where the break is. This keeps the bones from moving apart. Since bone is a living tissue, it produces new cells. The bones grow back together.

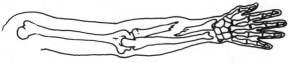

Simple Frature—break in bone, skin is closed

Compound Fracture—causes an open wound through which bone fragments may protrude

Osteoporosis

Osteoporosis is a bone disease. It happens when the bones lose too much calcium. This lack of calcium causes the bones to get brittle. They break easily. The bones actually shrink in size. A person with osteoporosis seems to shrink, too. This disease affects older females in particular. Doctors recommend that people drink enough milk and eat enough dairy products to prevent this disease. Regular exercise also strengthens the bones.

CHECK YOUR UNDERSTANDING

1. List four long bones in the body.
2. What do the vertebrae do?
3. List the organs protected by the ribs.
4. Give the common name for each of these bones: cranium, femur, and pelvis.
5. How does a doctor treat a fracture?
6. How can you prevent osteoporosis?

A joint is the meeting place of two bones. Joints allow the body to bend and move.

How Bones Move Together

Separate but together—that is how the skeletal system works. The 206 separate bones stay together and work together. The joints and muscles make this possible. Bending, twisting, and moving result from how the bones relate to each other.

Joints Are for Joining

The place where two bones join together is called a **joint**. If you look at the word joint, you can see that it is almost the same as the word join.

How do bones do this? Tough bands of tissue called **ligaments** join the bones together. Ligaments are elastic and move easily.

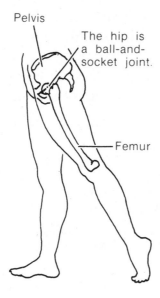

Pelvis

The hip is a ball-and-socket joint.

Femur

How Joints Move

Joints are the key to movement. They can move in several different ways, depending on what they have to do. The most flexible joint in your body is the **ball-and-socket joint**. It can allow movement all around. Your shoulder and hip are this kind of joint. In your hip, the top of your femur is shaped like a ball. It fits into a socket in your pelvis. You can move your femur forward and backward, from side to side, and around in a circle. You can move your shoulder in the same ways.

Your knee is a **hinge joint**. It allows the lower parts of your leg to move as a door on a hinge does. You can bend your knee so that your calf touches the back of your thigh. But you cannot bend your knee the other way.

Your elbow works in a similar way. It can move like a hinge joint, but it can also rotate. This is why your elbow is called a **pivot joint**. The place where your head meets your backbone is also a pivot joint.

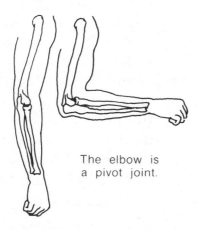

The elbow is a pivot joint.

Gliding joints are located in the spinal column. This column is made up of vertebrae. The vertebrae are connected by gliding joints. This arrangement allows you to move your back easily.

There are no ligaments in your cranium. The bones there are fused together, which means they do not move.

Joint Injuries and Diseases

Sometimes, the moving parts of a joint get worn down from constant use. They can be damaged in sports. Doctors can treat these kinds of injury with different kinds of surgery or medicine or with physical therapy.

Arthritis may occur. This is a disease in which the joints become inflamed and sore. The joints become deformed and cannot move well.

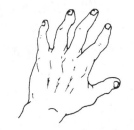

Arthritis stiffens joints.

Arthritis is usually treated with aspirin or other medicines that reduce inflamation and relieve pain. Doctors also recommend certain kinds of exercise.

From Cartilage to Bone

Before a baby is born, its skeleton is mostly **cartilage**. Cartilage is a strong, movable tissue containing calcium. The cartilage starts changing to bone even before birth. The bones are still too soft to allow the baby to walk. Babies also have soft skulls. This is why you have to be especially careful of a baby's head. As the baby grows, more and more cartilage turns to bone.

Some cartilage never becomes bone. We all have some cartilage in our bodies. Your nose is made of cartilage, and so are parts of your knees.

Calcium and Vitamin D

You probably have been told to drink plenty of milk in order to have strong bones and teeth. Doctors also advise pregnant women to drink milk to meet their needs and those of their developing baby.

Calcium is needed to change cartilage to bone. Since milk is a good source of calcium, it is good for bones. The body also needs vitamin D to be able to use the calcium. Some milk contains vitamin D. If it does, this information will appear on the milk container. The sun is another good source of vitamin D.

1. What does a joint do?
2. Name three kinds of joints. Give an example of each kind.
3. What is cartilage?
4. Why are calcium and vitamin D so important to the development of strong bones?

KEY IDEA #4:
Muscles are responsible for movement of the body and for certain activities within the body.

Muscles and Movement

Do you know that without muscles nothing in your body would move? When you think of muscles you probably think of working out in the gym or flexing your biceps. Muscles also work parts of the body when you do not even think about them. For example, your heart is really a muscle that pumps blood. Muscles line your stomach walls and push food down your digestive tract. There are muscle cells in the walls of your blood vessels. Muscles allow all parts of your body to move.

Look at the diagram of the muscular system in Appendix B at the end of the book as you read this section. It will help you become familiar with some muscles in the human body.

Voluntary or Involuntary

Muscles are classified as either voluntary or involuntary. Muscles that you cannot control are called **involuntary muscles**. These muscles function by themselves. You don't have to think about moving them. These kinds of muscles help body organs work. Some involuntary muscles force blood from the heart. Other involuntary muscles enable you to breathe, even when you are asleep.

Voluntary muscles are the muscles that are connected to your skeletal system. This is why they are also called **skeletal muscles.** Skeletal muscles are usually attached to the bones by tough tissues called **tendons**. Voluntary muscles can be moved at will. Learning to play games of skill involves training voluntary muscles.

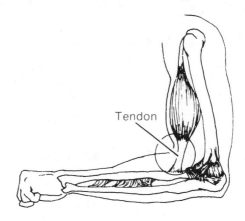

Tendon

How Muscles Work

Muscles work by contracting and relaxing. When a muscle contracts, it pulls on the tendon. Then, the tendon acts on the bone. The muscles, tendons, and bones all work together.

Some muscles work in pairs. When one muscle contracts, a related muscle relaxes. The **biceps** and **triceps** in the upper arm work like this. You can feel this happening. Bend your arm at the elbow. You can feel your biceps muscle contract while your triceps muscle relaxes. Now, extend your arm. Your biceps muscle is now relaxed and your triceps is contracted.

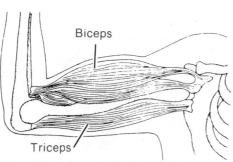

Biceps

Triceps

The Biceps Muscle Contracted

Some muscles never relax completely. They are partially contracted all the time. This tension holds up your body. This state of partial muscle contraction is called **muscle tone**.

Muscles and Exercise

You must use skeletal muscles often, or they will become weak and flabby. Regular exercise keeps muscles strong and healthy. It also strengthens bones and joints. Muscles can be strong without being big and bulging. You can be in good shape without looking like a contestant in a body-building contest.

After exercising hard or participating in a new sport, your muscles may hurt. The pain is due to two things: your muscles do not have enough oxygen, and they have too many waste products. Just like other cells, muscle cells take oxygen from the bloodstream. They use it to do their work. As they move, they form waste products.

The harder you exercise, the more oxygen the muscles need. They also have to get rid of more chemical waste. If you continue to exercise regularly, your heart will become accustomed to this need. It will pump more oxygen-carrying blood to the muscles. Practice improves efficiency. When you use muscle you won't lose it.

Muscle Injuries

You can injure a muscle if you fall or someone hits you hard. The muscle will actually tear and some blood will leak out. This causes a discolored skin mark we call a **bruise**.

You can strain a muscle if you work too hard. Athletes often tear muscles and tendons. In such a case, they may need an operation to repair this damage.

Muscular Dystrophy

Muscular dystrophy is a disease in which muscle fiber is gradually destroyed. Eventually, the arms and legs become useless. There is no cure for this disease at this time. Exercise and physical therapy can slow down the muscle deterioration.

1. What is the difference between voluntary and involuntary muscles?

2. What is a tendon?

3. Describe how some muscles work in pairs.

4. Why do muscles feel sore after hard exercise?

5. What makes your skin discolor when you get a bruise?

Summary of Chapter 5

The skeletal and muscular systems work together to allow you to move. Your bones give you support. If you did not have a skeleton, you would drop to the floor. Your skeleton keeps you upright and gives you your shape. It also protects your vital organs, such as the heart, lungs, and brain. Marrow, a substance inside some bones, makes blood cells.

There are 206 separate bones in your body. They are shaped in a variety of ways. The long bones in your arms and legs allow you to move. The vertebrae, which make up your spinal column, make your back flexible and protect your spinal cord. Spinal cord injuries can result in paralysis. The ribs protect the heart and lungs. The cranium protects your brain. Fractured bones can grow back together, because bones are made of living tissue.

A joint is a place where two bones meet. Ligaments connect the bones. The ball and socket joint, the hinge joint, the pivot joint, and the gliding joint are some of the joints in the body. Arthritis is a disease of the joints. The joints become inflamed and sore.

Muscles move your bones, with or without your thinking about it. There are involuntary and voluntary muscles. Muscles work by contracting and relaxing. Sometimes they do this in pairs. Like most every part of your body, muscles need regular exercise. If you exercise too hard, your muscles might hurt. This is because they are not getting enough oxygen and have too many waste products. Your heart will take care of this problem if you continue to exercise. You can injure a muscle by bruising it or straining it. Muscular dystrophy is a disease that destroys muscle fiber.

WORDS TO USE

1. bones
2. muscles
3. skeletal system
4. ribs
5. cranium
6. cells
7. tissues
8. calcium
9. marrow
10. femur
11. pelvis
12. tibia
13. fibula
14. ulna
15. radius
16. humerus
17. vertebrae
18. spinal cord
19. spinal column
20. backbone
21. sternum
22. fracture
23. osteoporosis
24. joint
25. ligament
26. ball-and-socket joint
27. hinge joint
28. pivot joint
29. gliding joints
30. arthritis
31. cartilage
32. involuntary muscles
33. voluntary muscles
34. skeletal muscles
35. tendons
36. biceps
37. triceps
38. muscle tone
39. bruise

REVIEW QUESTIONS FOR CHAPTER 5

1. What would you look like without your skeleton?
2. List the organs protected by the ribs and the cranium.
3. Why are bones classified as living tissue?
4. What are the two bones of the lower leg?
5. Why are bones so light?
6. Why are spinal cord injuries so serious?
7. Why should you wear a helmet when you play contact sports or ride a motorcycle?
8. How do doctors fix fractures?
9. What is osteoporosis?
10. Which part of the jaw can you move?
11. Where are joints located?
12. What are ligaments?
13. Which type of joint moves the most ways?
14. Name two pivot joints in your body.
15. What is arthritis?
16. How does milk help your bones?
17. What are involuntary muscles?
18. What are skeletal muscles?
19. How does regular exercise help your muscles and bones?
20. Why do your muscles need more oxygen when you exercise hard?

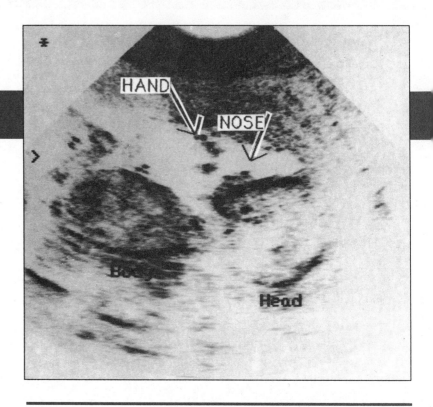

CHAPTER GOALS:

To understand the structure and function of the reproductive system.

To relate the function of the reproductive system to the beginning, growth, and development of a new individual.

To recognize some of the common sexually transmitted diseases.

KEY IDEAS:

The male reproductive system is made up of organs and glands that function to produce and deliver sperm.

The female reproductive system is made up of organs and glands that function to develop eggs and to prepare for the events that take place during pregnancy.

Sexually transmitted diseases (STDs) are infectious diseases that are spread through sexual contact.

CHAPTER 6

Reproduction

Males and females each have a different **reproductive system**. The structure and the parts of each system are different. The reproductive system is the only body system in which the structures and their functions are not identical in males and females. The male and female reproductive systems complement each other. Each reproductive structure has certain **functions**. Functions are actions or activities.

A male's reproductive system must make and deliver **sperm**. Sperm are male sex cells. The female reproductive system must make and deliver **eggs**. Eggs are female sex cells. In addition, the female reproductive system must receive the sperm and provide a place for the development of the **fertilized egg**. A fertilized egg results from the joining of an egg and a sperm.

Through the process of cell division, the fertilized egg grows and develops. At first, the developing human being is called an **embryo**. Later in its development, it is referred to as a **fetus**. The embryo and fetus are stages in the early growth of a human being.

From just two cells—an egg from the mother and a sperm from the father—a whole new individual develops. The male and female reproductive systems work together to produce babies. The babies become part of the family. Life continues.

The Male Reproductive System

Boys go through many physical changes between the ages of twelve and fifteen. This time is called **puberty**. It is also known as the time of passage that marks the change from childhood to manhood. Some tribal civilizations celebrate with tests that challenge the young males of the tribe. If the young males pass these tests of physical ability and endurance, they are admitted to manhood. It is a very important part of the lives of all members of the tribe.

Most of you who are studying health now are in this period of growth and change. You are developing into an adult. Most of the changes you notice are caused by chemicals from the glands. Some of the changes take place inside the body, in the reproductive system.

The Testes and Testosterone

The **testes** are the chief glands in the male reproductive system. One function of the testes is to make sperm. Beginning at puberty, sperm are made in large numbers every day. The testes also make the male hormone **testosterone**. During puberty, testosterone influences the growth of bone, muscle, and hair. This hormone also causes changes that result in a teenage boy's voice to becoming lower. Testosterone is a powerful chemical that directs the activities that cause the characteristics of "maleness" to develop.

About the Sperm

Sperm are very small. They can be seen only with the aid of a microscope. More than 1,000 of these cells would fit in the space taken up by the period at the end of this sentence. The sperm cell contains one-half the genetic material needed to begin the life of a whole new person. The other one-half of the genetic material comes from the female sex cell, or egg. Every day, millions of sperm are made in the testes. When sperm are released from the body or die, new ones take their place.

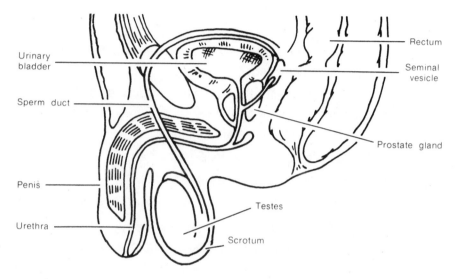

Male Reproductive System

The main purpose of sperm is to provide genetic material. In order to contribute to the beginning of a new individual, sperm must leave the male's body. From the testes, sperm pass through tubes that lead to the **penis**.

The penis is the external male sex organ. It has a large number of small blood vessels. When these vessels are filled with blood, the male has an **erection**; his penis becomes larger and firmer. In this state, the penis provides a passageway for the sperm to travel from the male to the female. During **sexual intercourse**, fluid called **semen** is transferred into the female's body. Semen contains the sperm.

The sperm that are released during sexual intercourse number in the millions. In general, only one sperm fertilizes the egg. Sperm that are near the egg release a chemical that dissolves part of the wall around the egg. This chemical is called an **enzyme**. As soon as one sperm enters the egg, the wall is sealed off. Thus, only one out of the millions of sperm actually fertilizes the egg. The other sperm die.

CHECK YOUR UNDERSTANDING

1. Why is the reproductive system different from any other body system?
2. What is the difference between structures and functions in body systems?
3. Give the name for male sex cells.
4. What are female sex cells called?
5. How does an egg become fertilized?
6. List the two stages in the early growth of a human.
7. What is puberty?
8. List some changes that take place in young males during puberty.
9. Where are male sex cells produced?
10. What is testosterone?

The female reproductive system is made up of
organs and glands that function to develop eggs and
to prepare for the events that take place in
pregnancy.

The Female Reproductive System

Between the ages of eleven and fourteen, girls go
through puberty. During puberty, girls undergo major
body changes. Much of the change takes place in the
reproductive system. The changes that take place in
boys and girls are similar in many ways. The changes in
both boys and girls are controlled by chemicals called
hormones. These changes move a girl from childhood
toward womanhood.

Estrogen and Development

Reproduction is important to the survival of every
species. Humans are no exception. During puberty,
females become ready for reproduction. Development
of their reproductive system takes place. This
development involves changes that are controlled by
the hormone **estrogen**. Estrogen is a female hormone. At
puberty, it activates many body changes, including
broadening of the hips and growth of the breasts.
Estrogen also causes the growth of underarm and **pubic
hair**. Pubic hair is the hair that grows in the genital
region.

During puberty, females begin to **ovulate**, or produce
eggs. The regular occurrence of ovulation means that
females are able to get **pregnant**. The ability to have
babies is a major step in the process of changing from a
girl to a woman.

The Ovaries

The **ovaries** are the female sex glands where eggs begin their development. The two ovaries are located in the lower abdomen. They have two major jobs. The first is to store the female's lifetime supply of egg cell material. The egg cell starts developing in the ovaries.

Besides serving as a storehouse, the ovaries also produce hormones, chiefly estrogen.

Immature egg cells are present in a female's body from the beginning of her life. Egg cells develop from them. About once a month, beginning at puberty, a mature egg is made ready for possible fertilization. The eggs grow and develop in structures inside the ovaries called **follicles**, or egg sacs. About 400 eggs develop during a female's reproductive years.

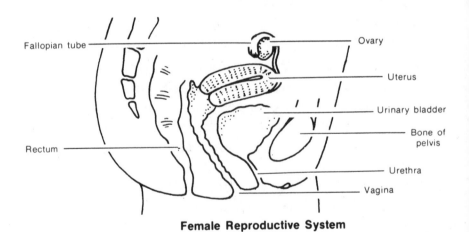

Female Reproductive System

The process of getting ready for the reproduction of life is directed by the **pituitary gland**. This gland sends out chemical signals that cause estrogen to be released. Estrogen plays a large part in preparing a place for the fertilized egg to develop.

Ovulation

The release of a mature egg from the follicle where it developed is known as **ovulation**. The egg is mature and ready to be fertilized. Ovulation is just one step in a cycle that is repeated every twenty-eight days. When ovulation takes place, the follicle acts like a gland. Glands make hormones. The follicle gland is called the **corpus luteum**. The corpus luteum manufactures a hormone called **progesterone**. The word progesterone is made from the prefix pre-, which means 'before," and the word gestation, which means pregnancy. This prepregnancy hormone causes changes in the wall of the **uterus**, or womb. The wall thickens and develops many small blood vessels in preparation to receive the fertilized egg.

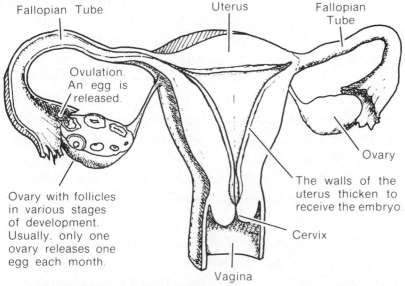

Fallopian Tube

Uterus

Fallopian Tube

Ovulation. An egg is released.

Ovary

Ovary with follicles in various stages of development. Usually, only one ovary releases one egg each month.

The walls of the uterus thicken to receive the embryo.

Cervix

Vagina

Fertilization and Gestation

It takes about fourteen days for an egg cell to ripen and be released. Ovulation signals a time when fertilization can take place. The egg can be fertilized for a period of about twenty-four hours. **Fertilization** is the union of an egg and a sperm. Sperm released in the **vagina** travel to the **fallopian tubes** after sexual intercourse. A mature egg is present in the fallopian tubes on the day that ovulation occurs.

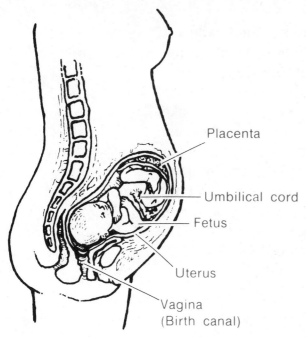

Placenta

Umbilical cord

Fetus

Uterus

Vagina
(Birth canal)

Fetus at Ninth Month of Pregnancy

If the egg is fertilized, it will travel down the fallopian tube and come to rest in the uterine wall. This wall is the perfect resting place for the fertilized egg. The egg will stay there and develop during the period known as pregnancy. Throughout preg-nancy, the baby will be nourished by means of the mother's blood. The period of pregnancy, or **gestation**, lasts for nine months in humans.

Twins

The ovaries usually release only one mature egg each month. Sometimes, something else happens. Two eggs may be released. Each egg can be fertilized by a single, separate sperm. Both of the fertilized eggs move down the fallopian tube and become embedded in the uterine wall. Both the eggs begin to develop. The result is **fraternal twins**. These twins may be two brothers, two sisters, or a brother and a sister. They are as alike and as different as any brothers and sisters.

Another kind of twinning sometimes takes place. **Identical twins** result when a single fertilized egg divides into two parts. Each part develops separately, and twins are born. The genetic makeup of each twin is identical to that of the other. Both individuals come from the same egg and the same sperm. The two are identical. They are both of the same sex.

What If the Egg Is Not Fertilized?

Most of the time, the eggs that develop during an **ovarian cycle** are not fertilized. Ovulation can only take place during one twenty-four-hour period. This is usually around the fourteenth day of the twenty-eight-day cycle.

The mature but unfertilized egg moves down the fallopian tube. The extra blood vessels that have built up in the walls of the uterus are no longer needed. The egg dissolves. It is discharged, along with the uterine lining, through the vagina. This natural process is called **menstruation**. Females menstruate for about five days during their monthly cycle. The first day of menstrual flow marks the first day of this cycle. The hormones estrogen and progesterone direct this monthly process.

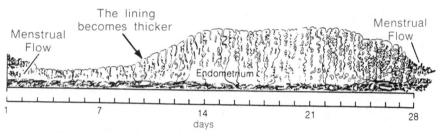

The Menstrual Cycle. Every month the lining of the uterus, or endometrium, gets ready to receive an egg. If the egg is not fertilized the woman does not get pregnant. The egg and the lining leave her body as the menstrual flow.

CHECK YOUR UNDERSTANDING

1. When do girls go through puberty?
2. Which hormone controls the development of the female reproductive system?
3. What are two changes that a female's body undergoes during puberty?
4. What is the connection between ovulation and pregnancy?
5. Name the chief hormones that are produced in the ovaries.
6. Where do immature egg cells grow and develop?
7. What is the corpus luteum?
8. Define fertilization.
9. What are the different kinds of twins that can develop?
10. How long is the ovarian cycle?

Sexually Transmitted Diseases

Sexually transmitted diseases, or STDs, are infectious diseases that are spread through sexual contact. Bacteria, viruses, fungi, and protozoa that cause these diseases need special environments to survive. They thrive in the warm, moist conditions inside the human body. Sexually transmitted diseases are a serious problem throughout the world. Millions of people in the United States are already infected with STDs. More than a million new cases are reported each year. Today, STDs are epidemic in the United States. In other words, they affect a large number of people at the same time.

Sexually transmitted diseases are most likely to occur among people between the ages of fifteen and thirty. In the United States, many people under the age of twenty-five have STDs. They can also occur in younger and older persons, but not as frequently. People who make a practice of changing sex partners run a greater risk of getting STDs.

Examples of sexually transmitted diseases are gonorrhea, chlamydia, syphilis, genital herpes, and AIDS. While these are the major STDs, there are others. Almost all sexually transmitted diseases are prevent-able. Most sexually transmitted diseases can be cured. But there are some that cannot be cured. AIDS and genital herpes are two STDs that cannot, at present, be cured.

Gonorrhea

Gonorrhea is spread by sexual contact. Since it is caused by a bacterium, it can be cured by using an antibiotic. One of these antibiotics is penicillin.

Antibiotics are available only through a doctor's prescription.

In males, gonorrhea results in an infection of the **urethra**. The urethra is the tube that leads from the bladder. This infection causes a discharge of pus from the penis. Another symptom, or sign, of this disease is a strong burning sensation during urination.

Gonorrhea can be particularly serious for women. About half the women who have this disease never show any of its symptoms. If this STD is not treated, it can cause the fallopian tubes to get inflamed. This can block the tubes and cause severe pain. The woman who has this condition may become **sterile**. This means that she cannot get pregnant. Women with gonorrhea who do give birth may pass this disease on to the child. It may cause the newborn baby to be blind.

Chlamydia

In women, the symptoms of **chlamydia** include abdominal pain and vaginal itching. Chlamydia may spread through the entire reproductive system. It can affect a developing baby.

Men who have this disease feel a burning sensation when they urinate. They may also experience pain and a discharge from the urethra. These symptoms are somewhat like those of gonorrhea, but they are less intense.

Doctors use the antibiotic tetracycline to treat chlamydia. If infected people do not get treatment, they may become sterile.

Syphilis

Syphilis is a serious STD. One of the early symptoms of syphilis is open sores. Doctors can diagnose syphilis by looking at these sores, or by using a blood test.

Like gonorrhea, syphilis is caused by a bacterium. Therefore, it can be treated with penicillin or other drugs. If it is not treated early, it can lead to blindness, mental illness, or other serious disorders, such as heart disease and paralysis.

Syphilis is mostly acquired through sexual intercourse. It results from direct contact with the infection in another person. A pregnant woman can pass the disease directly to her unborn baby. Syphilis is not picked up from toilet seats, towels, sheets, or other objects.

Genital Herpes

Genital herpes is another kind of STD. It is known by its general name: herpes. Unlike gonorrhea and syphilis, it is caused by a virus. There is no known cure for this disease.

Herpes shows up as blisters in the genital area. Headache, fever, and aching muscles often accompany the blisters. Herpes blisters appear, disappear, and then recur. The herpes infection can lie dormant for years. The herpes virus is transmitted through sexual contact.

Herpes symptoms are most painful in women. Genital blisters are especially painful during urination. In addition, herpes blisters can cause infection of a baby during the birth process. Women who have repeated infections of the herpes virus also have a higher risk of cancer.

Herpes is the fastest growing STD. It is considered to be epidemic. Without a cure, the epidemic continues. However, doctors can prescribe drugs to help the blisters dry up and heal faster.

AIDS—Acquired Immune Deficiency Syndrome

AIDS is an infectious disease. It is contagious, but it cannot be spread in the same manner as the common cold or measles or chicken pox. It is contagious in the same way that sexually transmitted diseases, such as gonorrhea and syphilis, are contagious. AIDS can also be spread through the sharing of intravenous drug needles and syringes used for injecting illicit drugs.

—Surgeon General's Report on AIDS

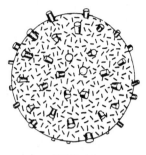

An AIDS Virus.
Highly Magnified

Since 1981, the disease known as AIDS has been in the news. AIDS is a lethal STD that is caused by a virus that attacks the body's immune system and eventually destroys the body's ability to fight off other diseases. Because it is, at this time, an incurable, deadly disease, it has caused great fear, concern, and misunderstanding. Its continued presence has made it a major concern of medical and health professionals all over the world. **Acquired Immune Deficiency Syndrome**, or AIDS, is a killer.

AIDS is caused by a **retrovirus** named HTLV-III. This virus attacks white blood cells. The virus is called a retrovirus because of the way it behaves in the host cells. Although this virus has been found in semen, blood, saliva, and tears of AIDS patients, there is no evidence that the virus can be transmitted through saliva or tears.

AIDS destroys a person's immune defense system. Normally, your body can defend itself against infection. AIDS destroys the body's ability to do this. Some symptoms of AIDS include fever, coughing, shortness of breath, and body sores.

AIDS is an infectious disease. The virus is most often acquired through sexual contact with an infected person or by sharing infected needles. AIDS is not spread through common, everyday contact. There is no evidence that family members living with AIDS-infected individuals become infected. In addition, a study of health workers who treated AIDS patients showed that the AIDS virus is not transmitted by casual contact.

Early on, AIDS seemed to be restricted to certain high-risk groups, including homosexual men and intravenous drug users. But others, including young children, have been infected and AIDS is no longer a disease of just those high-risk groups.

There is no cure for AIDS at this time, and no vaccine is available to prevent AIDS. Research aimed at finding a cure or a vaccine is being done by universities, the government, and private industry. Controlling certain behaviors can limit the spread of AIDS as can knowing how AIDS can be contracted and, equally important, how it cannot be contracted.

Knowing the facts about AIDS can prevent the spread of the disease. Education of those who risk infecting themselves or other people is the only way we can stop the spread of AIDS. People must be responsible about their sexual behavior and must avoid the use of intravenous drugs and needle sharing.

—Surgeon General's Report on AIDS

CHECK YOUR UNDERSTANDING
1. What do the initials STD stand for?
2. What is the meaning of the word epidemic?
3. What are two symptoms of gonorrheal infection in males?
4. What are the dangers of gonorrhea in females?
5. How is syphilis acquired and spread?
6. How is syphilis treated?
7. What causes genital herpes?
8. Name two incurable STDs.
9. How is the AIDS virus spread?
10. What does the immune defense system do?

Summary of Chapter 6

The human reproductive system is different in males and females. The function of the male system is to make and deliver sperm. The female system is centered around egg production. The female reproductive system is also structured to receive sperm and to carry out the stages of pregnancy.

Puberty is the time of life when males and females become sexually mature, or able to reproduce. Males make sperm, and females make eggs. Other bodily changes occur as maturity is reached. Much of the change is caused by hormones produced in the ovaries and testes. In females, estrogen and progesterone provide chemical directions. The hormone testosterone directs the changes that a male undergoes.

Ovulation, preparation for pregnancy, and menstruation are female reproductive activities that take place in a regular cycle. Fertilization of an egg leads to the development of a fetus. After gestation, birth occurs. Single births are normally the case, but twinning can happen. Fraternal or identical twins are possibilities.

Sexually transmitted diseases, or STDs, are diseases involving sexual contact. These diseases are transmitted through bacteria, viruses, fungi, or protozoa. In the United States, STDs are considered to be epidemic.

Most all of the sexually transmitted diseases are preventable. If contracted, some are curable. Genital herpes and AIDS are exceptions. At this time, there is no known cure for these diseases.

The Surgeon General's Report on the AIDS epidemic provides important information about how the disease is transmitted, the relative risks of infection, and how to prevent infection.

WORDS TO USE

1. reproductive system
2. functions
3. sperm
4. eggs
5. fertilized eggs
6. embryo
7. fetus
8. puberty
9. testes
10. testosterone
11. penis
12. erection
13. sexual intercourse
14. semen
15. enzyme
16. hormones
17. estrogen
18. pubic hair
19. ovulate
20. pregnant
21. ovaries
22. follicles
23. pituitary gland
24. ovulation
25. corpus luteum
26. progesterone
27. uterus
28. fertilization
29. fallopian tubes
30. vagina
31. gestation
32. identical twins
33. fraternal twins (see identical twins, no. 32)
34. ovarian cycle
35. menstruation
36. sexually transmitted disease
37. STDs
38. gonorrhea
39. urethra
40. sterile
41. chlamydia
42. syphilis
43. genital herpes
44. Acquired Immune Deficiency Syndrome
45. AIDS
46. retrovirus
47. immune defense system

REVIEW QUESTIONS FOR CHAPTER 6

1. What are two ways in which the male and female reproductive systems vary?

2. What are two stages in the early growth of a human being?

3. What is the name for the time of life when boys' and girls' bodies change physically to become adults?

4. Define testosterone.

5. Where is testosterone made?

6. What makes it possible for only one sperm to enter the egg?

7. What is the function of estrogen?

8. What is the meaning of the term ovulation?

9. What do the ovaries do?

10. Where are the follicles and what do they do?

11. What is the meaning of the term gestation?

12. Why does menstruation take place?

13. What do the letters STD stand for?

14. What is an epidemic?

15. What causes gonorrhea?

16. How is chlamydia treated?

17. What causes syphilis?

18. What causes genital herpes?

19. What are some symptoms of herpes?

20. What do the letters AIDS stand for?

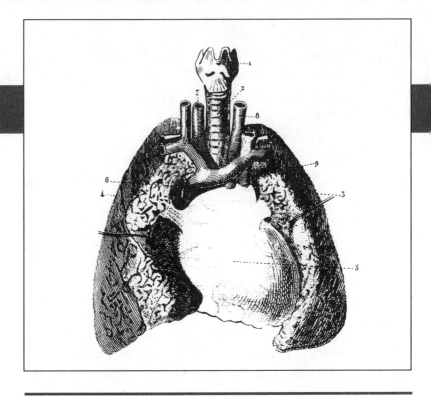

CHAPTER GOALS:

To describe how the respiratory, digestive, and excretory systems work.

To identify some of the major health problems that are associated with the respiratory, digestive, and excretory systems.

To suggest good health measures that can prevent these problems.

KEY IDEAS:

Respiration includes inhaling oxygen into the body to be used by the cells. It also involves removing carbon dioxide from the cells by exhaling.

Digestion begins in the mouth and continues in the stomach and small intestine.

The large intestines, the kidneys, the skin, and the lungs remove waste products.

Good health habits can prevent many problems of the respiratory, digestive, and excretory systems.

CHAPTER 7

The Respiratory, Digestive, and Excretory Systems

KEY IDEA #1:

Respiration includes inhaling oxygen into the body to be used by the cells. It also involves removing carbon dioxide from the cells by exhaling.

The Meaning of Respiration

When most people think of respiration, they think of breathing in and breathing out. If that is what you think respiration is, then you are exactly right. **Respiration** is the inhaling, or breathing in, of oxygen and the exhaling, or breathing out, of carbon dioxide. There is a system of tubes and organs that enables you to get the oxygen into your body and to get rid of the carbon dioxide. This system is called the **respiratory system**.

Do you know why you need oxygen? Do you know why you must get rid of the carbon dioxide? The body uses oxygen to break up the nutrients, or food, in the cells. Energy is released from the food. This process is called cellular respiration, or inner respiration. During cellular respiration, a waste product called carbon dioxide is produced. This waste product must be eliminated from the body.

Both processes described need to occur for cells to work properly. Without oxygen the cells would die. So would you. If the carbon dioxide wastes of cellular respiration were to collect in the bloodstream, the blood would become poisoned.

Respiration Begins in the Nose

You take in air through the **nostrils,** the openings at the end of the nose. Look at the diagram of the respiratory system. The nose is on the outside of the body. It is connected to a series of tubes and tissues that are inside the body. The nose and nostrils are part of the nasal passage. Air travels down the nasal passage, and through a long tube called the **trachea,** or windpipe.

You can also take in air through your mouth. Inhaling through your nose has some advantages. The lining of the nose contains tiny hairs that filter pollen and dust particles. Also, the tissues of the nose warm the air before it gets to the throat.

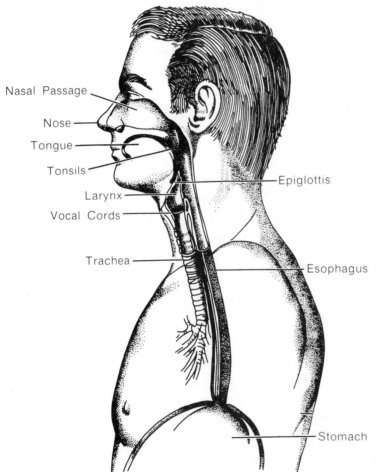

Nasal Passage
Nose
Tongue
Tonsils
Larynx
Vocal Cords
Trachea
Epiglottis
Esophagus
Stomach

Parts of the Respiratory System

Basic Health

Other Parts of the Respiratory System

Did you ever notice that your ears can feel blocked up or stuffy when you have a cold? The reason is that your nose and ears are connected by tubes called the eustachian tubes. For the same reason, your ears hurt when you blow your nose too hard.

The **tonsils** and **adenoids** are pieces of tissue at the back of the mouth cavity. They help destroy bacteria. However, these tissues can cause illness when they become inflamed and diseased. Tonsils and adenoids can be removed by simple surgery.

Notice that the trachea, or breathing tube, is right next to the food tube, or esophagus. What keeps food from entering the trachea and making you choke? At the entrance of the trachea, there is a small flap of tissue called the **epiglottis**. It can open and close. When it closes, food cannot enter the trachea.

The larynx, or voice box, contains two ligaments called vocal cords. Sounds are produced when the vocal cords vibrate. They vibrate whenever air is forced between the cords. Vocal cords work somewhat like the strings of a guitar. They can be "tuned" by changing their shape. When the cords are tight and short, they make a higher-pitched sound. When they are thicker, longer, and more relaxed, the vocal cords make a lower sound. Many voices are so distinct that a person can be identified or recognized by the sound.

The Bronchi and the Lungs

The trachea divides into two branches called the **bronchi**. The singular form of bronchi is bronchus. Each bronchus leads into one of the lungs. The lungs are the major breathing organs. Inside the lungs, the bronchi divide into smaller and smaller tubes called **bronchioles**. The smallest bronchioles keep on dividing until they finally join tiny sacs called **alveoli**. The walls of the alveoli are thin. They contain tiny blood vessels. Through these walls, gases are exchanged. Oxygen is the gas that comes in. Carbon dioxide is the gas that goes out.

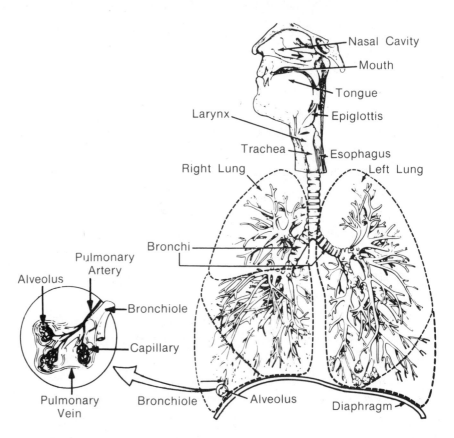

Exchanging Gases

The idea of exchanging gases may seem strange. What does it really mean? Oxygen and carbon dioxide are gases. When you inhale, you take into your lungs from the atmosphere air that contains oxygen. The alveoli transfer this oxygen into the bloodstream. From the lungs, the oxygen-rich blood travels to the heart. Once the blood is in the heart, it is ready to be pumped to all parts of the body. The body uses oxygen to break up food substances in the cells. Energy is released from the cells. In the process of releasing this energy, a waste product called carbon dioxide is formed. Carbon dioxide enters the bloodstream through tiny blood vessels and is carried back to the heart. The heart then pumps the blood, loaded with carbon dioxide, back to the lungs. The lungs exhale the carbon dioxide from the body. This process continues all through your life.

What Makes You Breathe

Together, the diaphragm and the rib cage cause the movement that actually enables you to breathe. The diaphragm is a band of muscle tissues that lie beneath the respiratory organs. The rib cage consists of thin, curved bones that surround the heart and lungs. Rib muscles allow the rib cage to move. The muscles of the rib cage and the diaphragm contract and expand. The chest cavity gets larger when the muscles contract and smaller when the muscles expand. These changes allow air to rush in and out of the lungs. The rate of breathing is an automatic process. When you exercise, this rate speeds up. It supplies extra oxygen to the cells and gets rid of extra waste products that are produced. The rate of breathing automatically slows down when you stop exercising.

CHECK YOUR UNDERSTANDING
1. List the places through which the air from the atmosphere travels from the time it enters the nostrils until it reaches the alveoli.
2. What is the difference between inhaling and exhaling?
3. Why is it better to breathe through your nose than through your mouth?
4. What does the epiglottis do?
5. How are your vocal cords like the strings of a guitar?
6. What are the bronchi?
7. Why does your body need oxygen?
8. What is the diaphragm?

Digestion begins in the mouth and continues in the
stomach and small intestine.

Love to Eat!

Do you love to eat? Do you crave chocolate cake?
Would you like some pizza, ice cream, steak, or french
fries? Are you hungry now? Is your mouth watering, even
though you are just thinking about food?

Most people love to eat and enjoy eating many
different kinds of food. Eating may be a pleasure. But it
is also a necessity. People need food to stay alive. The
cells in your body need the **nutrients** in food for energy,
growth, and repair.

The body cannot use food in the form of ice cream or
steak. Food must be changed into substances that the
cells can use. Changing, or breaking down, food into
simpler substances is called **digestion**.

Look at the diagram of the digestive system in
Appendix C at the end of the book as you read this
section. It will help you become familiar with the parts
of the digestive system.

Digestion Starts in the Mouth

When your mouth waters at the sight, smell, or thought
of food, what it really is doing is producing **saliva**. Saliva is
a liquid that is found in glands in your mouth. It contains a
special chemical that breaks down food. This chemical is an
enzyme. There are enzymes in all your digestive organs.
The enzyme in saliva breaks down starch. When you eat a
starchy food like potatoes or bread, the enzyme in the saliva
begins the process of digestion.

Your teeth and tongue also help digest food by
physical action. The tongue pushes food around. The
teeth chew the food into small pieces. As food is chewed,
it gets mixed up with saliva. The enzyme in the saliva
begins to chemically break down the food.

Down the Esophagus

The **esophagus** is a long tube that connects the mouth with the stomach. Food does not just drop through the esophagus into your stomach. It is pushed along by the muscles in the walls of the esophagus. Food can get to your stomach even if you eat while you lie down.

Into the Stomach

The stomach is another organ of digestion. It has two ways of breaking down food. The walls of the stomach secrete, or give off, gastric juices. Gastric juices contain enzymes that break down food chemically. The stomach also breaks down food by twisting and churning. Food remains in the stomach for three to four hours. During this time, the churning movement and the chemicals in the enzymes change solid food into a semiliquid form.

Digestion in the Small Intestine

Most of the body's digestion takes place in the **small intestine**. The small intestine is a curled-up tube located just below the stomach. If this tube were stretched out, it would measure about twenty-one feet, or nearly seven meters.

The **liver** and the **gallbladder** are special structures that help in the process of digestion. The liver is a large organ that produces **bile**. Bile helps digest butter and other fats. It breaks the fats into droplets. Bile acts somewhat the same way detergents do when they break up grease. The gallbladder is a pouch that is attached to the liver. The gallbladder stores bile. When bile is needed for digestion, it is pushed into the small intestine.

The **pancreas** is a **gland** that also helps in digestion. Glands are structures that secrete hormones. The pancreas produces a chemical called **insulin**, which helps the cells use sugar. The pancreas also secretes enzymes. These enzymes break down carbohydrates, proteins, and fats. Carbohydrates are found in starchy and sugary foods, such as bread and cake. Meat, fish, eggs, and cheese contain proteins. Margarine and cooking oil are examples of fats.

How Nutrients Get into the Blood

Nutrients in food must get into the bloodstream in order to be useful. After foods are chewed and churned and broken down into simpler substances, they are finally in a form that can be absorbed by the blood. How does food in this form get from the small intestine to the bloodstream?

The walls of the small intestine are lined with millions of tiny, fingerlike bulges called **villi**. Villi help absorb the nutrients. The villi contain tiny blood vessels, which are connected to the rest of the bloodstream. The villi absorb the digested food that has been broken down into chemicals. The chemical foods go into the blood vessels and get carried to all parts of the body by the bloodstream.

CHECK YOUR UNDERSTANDING

1. Describe two ways that foods are digested in the mouth.
2. What is the esophagus? Where is it located?
3. What happens to food while it is in the stomach?
4. Which gland helps in digestion in the small intestine? What does it do?
5. How does digested food get into the bloodstream?

KEY IDEA #3:
The large intestine, the kidneys, the skin, and the lungs get waste products out of the body.

Getting Rid of Wastes

You are a very efficient organism. You use all the nutrients, oxygen, and water that you need. If there is anything that you cannot use, you get rid of it. When you perspire, you eliminate water and salt through the skin.

You get rid of carbon dioxide and water when you exhale. You excrete undigested food and bacteria when you move your bowels. You eliminate other waste products when you urinate. These organs are all part of the **excretory system**.

The Large Intestine

Do you remember the process of digestion? Digestion begins in the mouth and ends in the small intestine, where the villi absorb the digested food. The villi do not absorb liquids, bacteria, undigested food, or dead cells. These products move on to the large intestine. This is a tube that is connected to the small intestine.

The large intestine absorbs water, minerals, and vitamins through its walls from the waste material. The solid material that remains in the large intestine is called **feces**. Feces are stored in the lower part of the large intestine. This part is called the **rectum**. Feces leave your body through an opening called the **anus** when you have a bowel movement.

The large intestine helps your body by gathering and removing the waste materials that are the by-products of digestion.

The Excretory System

The **kidneys** are the major organs of the excretory system. This means that they take wastes out of the blood. They also return useful materials such as glucose, water, and other substances needed for life to the blood as they do this work. Your two kidneys are located in the small of your back on either side of your spine. They are shaped like kidney beans.

As the blood supplies nutrients to the cells, waste products are formed. These wastes flow through cell membranes into the bloodstream. When the blood circulates through the kidneys, the waste products are removed. The kidneys contain tiny tubes called

nephrons. Nephrons filter waste products out of the blood. Filtered and purified, the blood travels back to the heart through the veins. The waste products travel out of the kidneys and into the bladder. The kidneys are useful in keeping fluid balance in your body. They are organs that regulate body fluids and substances.

When **urine**, a waste product, leaves the kidneys, it travels through long, narrow tubes to the **urinary bladder**. The urinary bladder is a stretchable bag that expands as it fills up with urine. Urine goes from the bladder into a tube called the **urethra**. The urethra takes the urine out of the body during urination. The urine removal system is part of the excretory system.

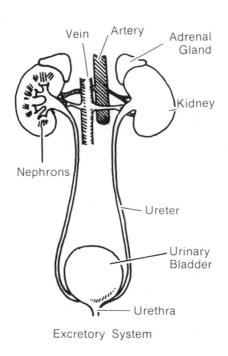

Vein   Artery   Adrenal Gland

Kidney

Nephrons

Ureter

Urinary Bladder

Urethra

Excretory System

Excretion by the Skin

As strange as it may seem, the skin is an organ. In fact, it is the largest organ of the body. The skin is the body's first line of defense against invading organisms. The skin not only covers the body, it also excretes waste. This waste product, called **perspiration**, is made up mostly of water. It also contains salts and urea. The skin contains thousands of tiny, coiled tubes called sweat glands. These glands open up at the surface of the skin. Perspiration leaves the skin through these openings, which are called pores.

Lungs Do Several Jobs

One of the waste products eliminated by the body is carbon dioxide. The lungs do this job by exchanging gases. With each breath, you inhale more oxygen than you exhale. You exhale more carbon dioxide than you inhale.

Blood transports the oxygen that you inhale to all the cells in your body. The cells combine oxygen with the nutrients from food to produce the energy the cells need. During this process, a waste product called carbon dioxide is formed. The blood carries carbon dioxide back to the lungs, where it diffuses from the blood to the lungs. The waste carbon dioxide is then exhaled. The lungs are involved in the respiratory system's work as well as in the excretory system's work.

CHECK YOUR UNDERSTANDING

1. How does the large intestine eliminate waste?
2. What are nephrons?
3. How is the urinary bladder able to hold urine?
4. Name the largest organ in the body.
5. What waste product do your lungs eliminate?

KEY IDEA #4:
Good health habits can prevent many problems of the respiratory, digestive, and excretory systems.

Good Health by Choice

Health problems that are associated with respiration, digestion, and excretion are very common. That is why you see so many advertisements for antacids and laxatives on television. It is also why you are constantly told not to smoke. Whether or not you smoke, what you eat, how much you eat, and how careful you are about your body are decisions that can determine the health of your respiratory, digestive, and excretory systems. These are some areas that affect your health that you can control. The right decisions can stop many problems before they start. There are some disorders that you cannot do anything about. Most times, though, common sense and good health habits will make your stomach feel better and your heart and lungs last longer. You will feel better, too.

Common Respiratory Problems

The most common respiratory problem is the cold. People point out that, although we have put a man on the moon, we still cannot cure the common cold. This is true. Fortunately, a cold usually causes no permanent damage, although it can make you miserable for a week. People have their own home remedies for curing a cold. Most doctors recommend aspirin, bed rest, simple foods, and plenty of liquids. Some physicians have advised treating a cold with large doses of vitamin C. Most doctors disagree. They say there is no scientific proof that large amounts of any vitamin make a difference.

Choking — A Respiratory Problem

Perhaps you do not think of choking as a problem of the respiratory system, but it is. Picture someone laughing and eating at the same time. A bone or a large piece of food could become lodged in the trachea, or windpipe. The victim would cough automatically and the food or bone might come out. What if it didn't? Would you know what to do if a person was choking?

At one time, some medical people sug-

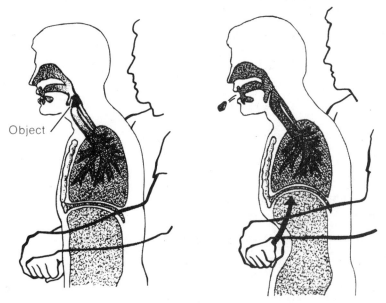

The Heimlich Maneuver. The force of your fists causes air in the victim's lungs to be expelled. The object will be ejected.

Object

gested slapping the victim on the back. Now they advise you to perform the Heimlich maneuver. This technique was named after Dr. Henry Heimlich, who perfected it. To perform the Heimlich maneuver, you should stand behind the victim. After you wrap your arms around the person, you should pull back and upward at a point right below the rib cage. A quick thrust should force the object up and out of the trachea. (See illustration on page 132.)

Sore Throats — Mild or Strep?

A sore throat is another common respiratory disorder. Most sore throats are due to colds or other mild infections. They are nothing to worry about. Sometimes, a sore throat can also mean that you have a strep infection. This can be more serious.

Strep is short for streptococcus, which is a kind of bacteria. A strep infection can lead to damage to your heart if it is not treated. A doctor can determine if you have a strep infection by doing a throat culture. In a throat culture, material is taken from your throat with a cotton swab. The material on the swab is allowed to grow in a laboratory. After a few days, your physician or lab technician will look at the culture under a microscope. Examination of the culture will tell whether it is strep or not.

If you do have a strep infection, the doctor will prescribe antibiotics to prevent serious complications. Naturally, you do not have to see a doctor every time you have a slight sore throat. But if you have a fever and your throat hurts a great deal, you should have a throat culture taken. Small children are more inclined to have strep infections, but adolescents and adults also can get strep.

Tonsillitis

Tonsillitis is a condition that occurs when the tonsils become infected. Although the purpose of the tonsils is to kill bacteria, sometimes so many germs are present in the throat that the tonsils themselves become diseased. The symptoms of tonsillitis are a sore throat, fever, and difficulty in swallowing. Tonsillitis is very common in young children. In the past, doctors would treat this condition by removing the tonsils. Now, however, tonsillitis can be cured by penicillin or another antibiotic.

The Flu

Influenza, or the flu, is a viral infection. That means that influenza is caused by a virus instead of bacteria. It also means that antibiotics will not be effective in treating the flu, because antibiotics work only on bacteria. However, doctors may prescribe antibiotics for someone who has the flu, because they are likely to come down with other infections. Flu symptoms include headache, fever, and general aches and pains. These symptoms usually last about a week.

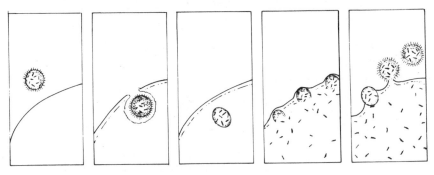

A flu virus lands on a lung cell. It buries itself and releases genes. The lung cell then makes many more viruses. The new viruses break out and attack other cells.

Chronic Bronchitis

Sometimes, when you have the flu or a cold, you develop a cough. Once the illness goes away, the cough usually stops, too. However, heavy smokers usually have a chronic cough—one that lingers for weeks or months after the illness is over. Smokers also tend to get **chronic bronchitis.**

Bronchitis is an infection of the bronchial tubes. It usually goes away in a short time if it is treated properly. But chronic bronchitis is different. Chronic means recurring over a long period of time. Most people who have chronic bronchitis are heavy smokers. Their bronchioles produce more mucus than normal. People with this disease cough and spit up phlegm.

Pneumonia

Pneumonia is a disease of the lungs in which the bronchioles and alveoli become infected. The symptoms are fever, chills, and discomfort when breathing. There are two types of pneumonia. One is caused by bacteria, and the other is caused by a virus. Bacterial pneumonia is more serious, because the entire lung can be affected. It must be treated immediately with antibiotics. Viral pneumonia may follow a cold. It is not as serious as bacterial pneumonia, but it still should be taken care of. It involves only patches of the lungs. It causes headaches, fever, and weakness.

Allergies

Allergies are the body's response to something disturbing in the environment. You probably have heard someone say, "I am allergic to bee stings," or "I cannot eat chocolate." They are talking about their allergies.

Sometimes, the body reacts to ordinary substances in an unusual way. There are people who develop hives when they come in contact with certain animals. Hives are large bumps on the body that hurt and itch. Some people cough or have difficulty breathing because they are allergic to a certain kind of plant.

Most allergies cause little difficulty. They can be treated with medicine bought from the drugstore. Some allergies are more serious. The doctor may have to prescribe a more powerful medicine. The person with an allergy may also decide to undergo treatments to be desensitized. For example, if you knew that you were allergic to timothy grass, a doctor would expose you to small amounts of the grass until you developed an immunity to the grass. The doctor would place small amounts of timothy grass on or under your skin until you were able to fight its effects. This would mean that you had built up an immunity to timothy grass. Of course, you would have another option: staying away from timothy grass. Treating an allergy has much to do with what the causing substance is, and how often the allergy sufferer comes into contact with it.

Hay Fever and Asthma

Ragweed

Hay fever and **asthma** are two common allergies. Hay fever is an allergic reaction to certain grasses, such as ragweed. People with hay fever usually suffer whenever ragweed is in bloom. People with hay fever often get shots for their allergy.

People with asthma are often sensitive to many substances. They wheeze and cough when they are affected. As with most other illnesses, asthma attacks are most likely to occur when a person is run down, is under a great deal of stress, or has a cold or other illness. Asthmatics usually know what will set off an attack. So, they are careful about what they do and with what they come in contact. Many people with asthma carry an inhalant or other medication with them. These medicines help people breathe if their asthma is very bad. Some attacks are so severe that a physician must give the victim a shot of cortisone or adrenaline.

A person with asthma uses an inhaler

Basic Health

Serious Respiratory Diseases

Emphysema and **lung cancer** are two very serious diseases of the respiratory system. These diseases are often preventable. Both emphysema and lung cancer occur more often in people who smoke. So you are more likely to get these diseases if you smoke.

Emphysema is a disease in which the tissues of the lung are destroyed. The symptoms of emphysema are shortness of breath and difficulty in breathing. People with emphysema cannot get enough air into their lungs. Even normal activities, such as sitting up or getting out of bed, are difficult. Emphysema is often listed as a cause of death.

Lung cancer also is a killer. Cancer is a disease in which cells multiply abnormally, causing a growth or tumor. Of all the cancers, lung cancer has the lowest cure rate. If only one lung is involved, that lung can be removed. It is possible to survive with just one lung. But, if the cancer strikes both lungs, other forms of treatment must be used. These include radiation and chemotherapy. Unfortunately, the success rate of these treatments is not very high. Since smoking is responsible for most lung cancers, the best advice is not to smoke.

Common Problems of Digestion

Gas, constipation, and diarrhea are probably the most common problems of digestion. Nausea, vomiting, and loss of appetite also occur frequently. Sometimes, all of these digestive problems can be lumped together under the common term indigestion.

Gas is not usually a serious problem, but it can be embarrassing. Gas is formed when you swallow air. Sometimes, eating and drinking too fast can produce an excess amount of gas. Certain foods, such as cabbage, broccoli, and beans, also form gas in certain people. A change in diet can help to stop this condition.

Diarrhea is a watery discharge of feces instead of a normal bowel movement. Diarrhea can be caused by bacteria in foods, by laxatives, or by emotional stress. People often get diarrhea after eating in restaurants that serve different or exotic foods or when visiting foreign countries.

Constipation is the opposite of diarrhea. In constipation, there is difficulty or pain when moving the bowels. Bowel movements are infrequent and irregular. Generally, this condition is caused by a diet that is too low in fiber foods. The addition of bran flakes, whole wheat bread, salads, and fresh fruits will add fiber, or bulk, to the diet. Fiber foods stimulate the muscles of the colon to get the waste out of the body. Changing the diet is a better plan for treating constipation than taking laxatives. Like fiber foods, laxatives also stimulate the colon. However, too many laxatives can irritate and damage the muscles of the colon.

Other Disorders of the Digestive System

Appendicitis is an infection of the appendix, a small organ located near the large intestine. The purpose of the appendix is to help the body resist disease. In appendicitis, the appendix becomes inflamed and tender. It may swell up so much that it bursts. When it bursts, it spills its poisonous contents into the area around it and causes further infection. A burst appendix can even result in death.

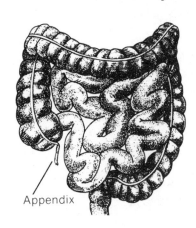
Appendix

The symptoms of appendicitis are pain, nausea, fever, and tenderness on the right side around the area of the appendix. Anyone with these symptoms should see a physician immediately. The appendix should be removed if the doctor diagnoses appendicitis, because the appendix is diseased and is not serving its purpose.

Gallstones are small, hard masses that form in the gallbladder. They can cause severe pain in the upper right section of the chest, around the ribs and shoulder. Gallstones can develop because of a diet that contains too much fat. In some cases, the gallstones must be removed surgically. Other times, a change in diet may help. Recently developed drugs may also be able to break up the stones.

Gallstones are hard masses that cause great pain.

Ulcers are open sores in the lining of the stomach or the small intestine. Some ulcers are caused by too much acid. It is normal to have acids in the stomach because acids help in the process of digestion. But, if there is too much acid, it can actually eat away at the lining of the stomach or small intestine. This causes swelling and pain. Sometimes, emotional stress causes the production of an excess amount of acid. Alcohol, tobacco, caffeine, and aspirin can also irritate the stomach walls. Antacids relieve the symptoms of ulcers, but doctors can prescribe even more effective medications.

Diseases of the Excretory System

Cystitis is a condition in which the urinary bladder is infected. This disorder is more common in women than in men. Women have a shorter urethra. This makes it easier for bacteria to enter the bladder. Symptoms of cystitis are the need to urinate frequently and burning or pain during urination. Antibiotics can usually stop this infection.

Kidney failure is the most serious problem of the urinary tract. The purpose of the kidneys is to get rid of waste products by purifying the blood. If this system breaks down, poisons remain in the blood. Disease and death will follow. A person can live with only one kidney. If both kidneys do not work, dialysis must be used. This is a process of artificially cleaning the blood. Dialysis takes over the work of the kidneys. In this kind of treatment, the blood vessels are connected to the dialysis machine. The blood then goes from the arteries into the machine, where it is purified. Then, the blood is returned to the body. Dialysis is a long and difficult process. People who have kidney failure must undergo this procedure about once a week for the rest of their lives.

Kidney transplants are another way of restoring kidney function to persons with kidney failure. In a transplant operation, a functioning kidney is taken from the donor and put into the body of the person to replace the kidney that does not function. Transplants are difficult because the body naturally rejects any foreign substance. A kidney from another person is, of course, a foreign substance. Doctors try to match donors to patients so that the kidney will not be rejected. Using a kidney from a twin or a close relative increases the chances that the kidney will be accepted. The use of newly discovered drugs has lessened the possibility of rejection.

CHECK YOUR UNDERSTANDING

1. What can be done to help a person who is choking?
2. What is tonsillitis?
3. What are two common allergies?
4. How can emphysema and lung cancer be prevented?
5. What are the most common problems of digestion?
6. What are the symptoms of appendicitis?
7. What are ulcers?
8. How does dialysis work?

Summary of Chapter 7

Respiration is the inhaling of oxygen and the exhaling of carbon dioxide. Air enters the body through the nostrils, continues down the nasal passage and trachea, and enters the lungs through the bronchi and bronchioles. Gases are exchanged through the alveoli in the lungs.

The digestive system breaks down food into a form that the body can use. Digestion begins in the mouth and continues in the stomach and small intestine. From the small intestine, digested food enters the bloodstream. Undigested food leaves the body through the large intestine.

Besides the large intestine, the urinary tract, the skin, and the lungs eliminate wastes from the body. The waste material of the kidneys is urine. Perspiration is excreted by the skin, and carbon dioxide is expelled from the lungs.

The cold is the most common respiratory problem. Influenza, tonsillitis, and bronchitis are other diseases of the respiratory system. The two most serious respiratory diseases are emphysema and lung cancer. The chances of getting these diseases are lessened by not smoking.

Many common digestive disorders, like gas and constipation, can be avoided by eating sensibly. Appendicitis is a disease that requires the immediate care of a physician. The most serious problem of the urinary tract is kidney failure. Without a kidney transplant, people with kidney failure must undergo dialysis for the rest of their lives.

WORDS TO USE

1. respiration
2. respiratory system
3. nostrils
4. trachea
5. tonsils
6. adenoids
7. epiglottis
8. bronchi
9. bronchioles
10. alveoli
11. nutrients
12. digestion
13. saliva
14. esophagus
15. small intestine
16. liver
17. gallbladder
18. bile
19. pancreas
20. gland
21. insulin
22. villi
23. excretory system
24. feces
25. rectum
26. anus
27. kidneys
28. urine
29. nephrons
30. urinary bladder
31. urethra
32. perspiration
33. influenza
34. tonsillitis
35. chronic bronchitis
36. pneumonia
37. allergies
38. hay fever
39. asthma
40. emphysema
41. lung cancer
42. diarrhea
43. constipation
44. appendicitis
45. gallstones
46. ulcers
47. cystitis
48. kidney failure

REVIEW QUESTIONS FOR CHAPTER 7

1. What is the name of the system that enables you to get oxygen and get rid of carbon dioxide?

2. Where does respiration begin?

3. Describe the trachea.

4. What are the alveoli?

5. Why do the cells in our body need the nutrients that are found in the food we eat?

6. Define the term *digestion*.

7. What is the function of the esophagus?

8. Describe how the stomach breaks down food.

9. Where does most digestion take place?

10. Where is bile produced? What does bile do?

11. What role does the pancreas play in digestion?

12. What job do the kidneys do?

13. What is the role of the skin in waste removal?

14. How is carbon dioxide eliminated from the body?

15. What is the best treatment for the common cold?

16. How is flu treated?

17. What is tonsillitis?

18. What is chronic bronchitis?

19. List the symptoms of pneumonia.

20. What is an allergy?

21. Describe asthma.

22. What is emphysema?

23. Give the cause of diarrhea.

24. What is a cause of constipation?

25. List the symptoms of appendicitis.

26. What causes gallstones?

27. What causes ulcers?

28. What is cystitis?

29. What is the purpose of dialysis?

30. Tell what happens in a kidney transplant.

CHAPTER GOALS:

To understand that good nutrition, regular exercise, and body care help you look and feel the best that you can.

To learn what the body needs in terms of food, exercise, and care of the teeth and skin.

KEY IDEAS:

Good nutrition and a balanced diet help prevent health problems.

The right number of calories for your body and regular physical activity keep you in good shape.

Taking care of your teeth, skin, and hair improves your appearance and prevents disease.

CHAPTER 8

Food, Appearance, and Fitness

KEY IDEA #1:
Good nutrition and a balanced diet help prevent
health problems.

Eating Right

"Drink four glasses of milk daily."

"Finish all the food on your plate."

"Don't eat all that junk food."

"Take a vitamin pill every day."

Does this advice sound familiar? Have you been
listening to suggestions like these all your life? Is this
really good advice? Do you need to drink milk? Is it
necessary to take vitamins? Read on and see.

Nutrition

Nutrition is the process of taking food into the body
and making use of that food. Nutrition means nourishing
or feeding the body with foods or **nutrients**. Nutrients
are the chemical substances the body needs to function.
Cells need nutrients for energy, growth, and repair.

Your body needs different nutrients.

You need many different kinds of foods in order to stay healthy. Eating only bread and meat, for example, will not give you all the nourishment or nutrients that you need. The body needs six different nutrients for good health. They are carbohydrates, proteins, fats, vitamins, minerals, and water.

Carbohydrates

Carbohydrates are chemical substances made of sugars and starches. Carbohydrates produce energy. During digestion, the body breaks down carbohydrates into a substance called **glucose**. Glucose is a form of sugar that is used by the body to provide energy. This is why a candy bar can be satisfying when you are hungry. The high sugar content converts quickly to glucose to provide you with instant energy. Excess glucose gets stored in the body as fat.

You can get the carbohydrates that you need by eating foods containing starches and sugars. Potatoes and grains are good sources of starches. Wheat, rye, rice, and corn are grain plants. They are used to make bread and cereals. **Cellulose** is another starch found in plants. Cellulose is the hard part of plants that cannot be digested. Even though cellulose is indigestible, it is still necessary for good health. Cellulose provides the body with fiber, or bulk. The muscles in the walls of the digestive tract work well as fiber passes through them. A high-fiber diet can prevent **constipation**. Constipation is a condition where solid wastes are not moved out of the body. Some studies show that cancer of the digestive tract may result from a diet that is too low in fiber.

Fruit is an excellent source of natural sugar. Candy, cake, and ice cream also contain sugar. These foods are made from processed, or refined, sugar. They taste good, but they do not provide the body with many vitamins and minerals. Too many sweets can cause tooth decay and cavities. Doctors advise you to get your supply of carbohydrates by eating more starches and fewer sugars. Starches keep glucose levels even. This keeps you from feeling tired.

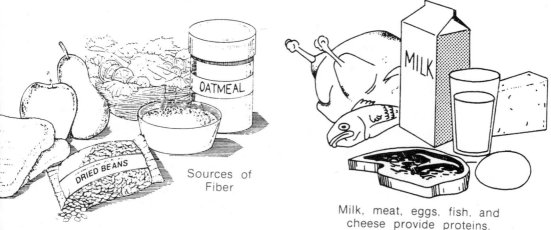

Sources of Fiber

Milk, meat, eggs, fish, and cheese provide proteins.

Proteins

Proteins are necessary for the repair and growth of tissues. They are also needed for body maintenance. The condition of the hair, skin, and nails depends upon an adequate supply of protein. Muscles and blood also need protein.

Proteins are large molecules. They are made from smaller chemical units, or building blocks, called **amino acids**. The body makes most of the amino acids it needs, but it cannot manufacture all of them. The amino acids that the body cannot manufacture are called **essential amino acids**. You need to eat proteins in order to give your body the essential amino acids that it needs.

Animal products like milk, meat, fish, and eggs provide all of the essential amino acids. Nuts, seeds, beans, breads, and cereals supply some of the essential amino acids. Some combinations of proteins eaten together provide all of the essential amino acids. A good example of this kind of combination is peanut butter and bread.

Fats

Like carbohydrates, **fats** also supply the body with energy. The difference is that fats are stored energy, or energy in reserve. Although you have probably heard about the harmful effects of fats, some fats in the diet are necessary. For example, fats help you digest certain vitamins. This does not mean that you have to eat extra fat. Even if you never have a pat of butter or a drop of oil, you can still get your fat supply from the other foods that you eat.

Why do fats have such a bad reputation? Certain kinds of fats lead to high levels of **cholesterol**. A high cholesterol level is one forerunner of heart disease. Cholesterol is a waxy substance that does no harm in normal amounts. However, when the cholesterol level gets too high, it becomes a problem. Then, cholesterol deposits build up inside the blood vessels and clog them. Blood cannot flow freely to and from the heart. This increases the chance of a heart attack.

Cholesterol buildup starts in childhood. You can prevent it from happening. You can limit the foods you eat containing fats that raise cholesterol levels. Fats can be classified according to their type. Some fats are saturated. Others are polyunsaturated. **Saturated fats** raise the cholesterol level. **Polyunsaturated fats** lower the cholesterol level.

Butter, lard, cream, cheese, whole milk, palm oil, coconut oil, and chocolate contain large quantities of saturated fats. Avoid these products as much as you can. Safflower, corn, cottonseed, and soybean oils are polyunsaturated fats. Use these products instead. In general, you should avoid eating fried foods. Use corn oil margarine instead of butter. Drink skim milk instead of whole milk. Eat more chicken, fish, and lean meats than red meats. Dieting habits like these will help to prevent cholesterol buildup.

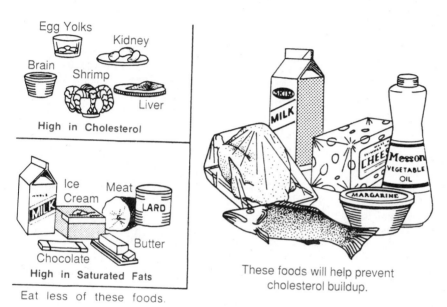

High in Cholesterol

Egg Yolks
Kidney
Brain
Shrimp
Liver

High in Saturated Fats

Ice Cream
Meat
LARD
MILK
Chocolate
Butter

Eat less of these foods.

These foods will help prevent cholesterol buildup.

Vitamins

Vitamins are useful substances found in different foods. They are necessary for good health. Vitamin D is needed for strong bones and teeth. Vitamin K is necessary for blood clotting. If you eat a balanced diet, you will get all the vitamins you need. You will not need to take vitamin pills. But, if you don't eat nutritious foods, you probably will have a vitamin deficiency. For example, a lack of vitamin A will make it difficult for you to see at night. Review the chart on essential vitamins to see how other vitamins can help you.

ESSENTIAL VITAMINS		
Vitamin and Source	What It Does	Deficiency Disease
Vitamin A Milk, egg yolk, beef liver, carrots, sweet potatoes, yellow squash, spinach and other greens	Helps skin, hair, eyes, and lining of nose and throat; prevents night blindness; promotes growth	Dry, rough skin, lowered resistance to respiratory infections, poor vision in twilight
Niacin Beef, chicken, and turkey; liver; whole wheat; milk; cereals; mushrooms	Protects skin and nerves, aids digestion	Mental depression, digestive disturbances, dermatitis
Vitamin B (Thiamine) Pork, sunflower seeds, whole grains, cereal, green beans, peanuts, organ meats	Protects health of nervouse system, aids appetite and digestion	Tiredness, loss of appetite
Vitamin B$_2$ (Riboflavin) Milk and milk products, pork, liver, eggs, bread, rolls, crackers, green leafy vegetables	Increases body resistance to infection, prevents harmful changes to eyes	Eye fatigue, lower vitality, inflammation of mouth and tongue
Vitamin C (Ascorbic acid) Tomatoes, most citrus fruits, potatoes, fruit juices, green pepper	Helps form bones and teeth, prevents scurvy, enhances iron absorption	Scurvy, sore joints, tender gums, poorly formed bones and teeth, poor wound healing
Vitamin D Fish oils, milk, sunlight	Prevents rickets, uses calcium and phosphorus to build bones and teeth	Rickets, poorly formed bones and teeth
Vitamin E Vegetable oils, margarine, asparagus, peaches	Helps maintain cell health, has possible role in reproduction	Breakdown of red blood cells, smokers have very low levels of vitamin E
Vitamin K Green leafy vegetables, soy beans, bran, peas, green beans, liver	Aids in clotting of blood	Bleeding

Minerals

Like vitamins, **minerals** are found in tiny amounts in the foods that you eat. They are also essential to good health. The minerals sodium and potassium help the cells to function and the heart to work well. Calcium and phosphorus build strong teeth and bones. You get all the minerals that you need if you eat a nutritious diet. You must eat good, nutritious foods each day, since minerals cannot be stored in the body.

One mineral that people generally consume too much of is **sodium**, or table salt. Some people use the salt shaker even before they taste their food. The problem with this habit is that it leads to an overuse of sodium. Sodium is associated with high blood pressure. High blood pressure is related to heart disease. People on restricted salt diets have learned to cook with other spices. They use a variety of herbs such as pepper, garlic, onion powder, and oregano.

Some canned and packaged foods contain large amounts of sodium. Labels can inform you about the amount of salt contained in a product. Packaged foods must identify the ingredients used in the product. That information is listed on the label. Be sure to read it carefully. The ingredient that is used the most is listed first. Look at a soup label. If sodium is the first or second ingredient, you know that the soup contains a great deal of salt.

One mineral that many women do not get enough of is **calcium**. A calcium deficiency, combined with a lack of exercise, can cause **osteoporosis**. Osteoporosis is a bone disease in which the bones become brittle and less dense. This can cause bones to break more easily. Women's

ZESTY
TOMATO
SOUP

INGREDIENTS:
Tomatoes, sugar, modified food starch, onions, salt, corn starch, dehydrated onions, dehydrated garlic, yeast extract, spice, citric acid, chives, dehydrated parsley, paprika, vitamin C (ascorbic acid), and turmeric.

bones are less dense to begin with, so they are more apt to be affected. Also, since women are more diet-conscious than men, they tend to drink less milk. This decreases their calcium supply. Both men and women need an adequate supply of calcium. Both need to have a regular exercise program in order to strengthen their bones. For more information, look at the chart about minerals.

Water

Water is not a food, but it is still considered a nutrient because you cannot live without it. Water is needed for the chemical reactions that go on inside your body. Your blood is mostly water. In fact, your body is about 70% water. Water is lost when you breathe out, perspire, or urinate. You need to replace this water. You can do this by drinking or eating. Most foods have water in them. If too much water is lost, the body will dehydrate, or dry out.

A Good Diet

You probably already have some idea about a good diet. You know what the right foods are. You need carbohydrates, proteins, fats, vitamins, minerals, and water. You probably know that too much refined sugar causes cavities and that too much sodium is related to high blood pressure. You have learned that eating saturated fats can lead to heart disease. You know that a lack of vitamins or minerals can result in deficiency disorders. But how do you put all that information together into some kind of a meal plan? How can you be sure that you are getting all the nutrients that you need?

The Four Basic Food Groups

Food is usually divided into four major food groups the milk group, the meat group, the vegetable-fruit group, and the bread-cereal group. One way to ensure that your body is getting the necessary nutrients is to select foods from each of the four groups during each day.

SOME ESSENTIAL MINERALS		
Mineral and Source	What It Does	Deficiency Disease
Sodium In most foods, table salt	Maintains internal fluid balance, helps nerve transmission	Muscle cramps, weakness
Potassium Bananas, oranges, milk	Maintains internal fluid balance, helps nerve transmission	Heart disturbances
Calcium Milk products, green and leafy vegetables	Helps to form bones and teeth, helps heart action	Bowed legs, osteoporosis
Phosphorus Protein products	Helps to form bones and teeth, produces energy	Irritability, weakness
Magnesium Green and leafy vegetables, nuts, whole grains	Helps form bones and teeth, helps nerve action	Muscle weakness, heart disturbances
Iron Kidney, liver, beans, beef	Helps form red blood cells	Anemia, tiredness
Iodine Seafoods, iodized salt	Helps the thyroid gland work	Enlarged thyroid gland

Some nutritionists add a fifth group to the list. It is called the snack group, or empty calorie group. Alcoholic beverages, soft drinks, and sugary snack foods are in this group. A carbonated beverage, for example, generally contains no protein, no calcium, no iron, no vitamins, and no minerals. Then what is in it? Only calories! Do you really need this fifth group?

FOUR BASIC FOOD GROUPS

Food Group	Foods in Group	Daily Requirement
Milk Group	Milk, butter, cheese, ice cream	4 glasses or their equivalent
Meat Group	Meats, poultry, eggs, peas, dry beans, nuts	2 or more servings
Vegetable-Fruit Group	Dark green and yellow vegetables, citrus fruits, tomatoes	4 or more servings
Bread-Cereal Group	Bread, cereals, crackers, pasta	4 or more servings

CHECK YOUR UNDERSTANDING

1. Define nutrition.
2. List the six different nutrients.
3. What is glucose?
4. List foods that are a source of carbohydrates.
5. Why does the body need cellulose?
6. Why is it better to get your carbohydrates from starches than from sugar?
7. What does protein do for the body?
8. Which nutrients give the body energy?
9. Why are polyunsaturated fats better for you than saturated fats?
10. How does cholesterol contribute to heart disease?

Looking Good

People are always talking about how a good diet keeps you healthy and how nutritious meals prevent diseases. These ideas sound correct to you. You want to keep your health. You certainly do not want to come down with any diseases because of the wrong diet. But that is not all you want. You also want to look the best that you can. What does that have to do with the food that you eat?

Everything! A combination of nutritious food, the right amount of calories, physical activity, and enough sleep will help you look your best. Your muscles will be toned. Your skin and hair will look better. Best of all, you will have more energy to do all the things you want to do.

Calories

A **calorie** is a unit used for measuring heat. Different foods have different caloric values. The more active you are, the more calories you burn up. Teenage girls need about 2100 to 2200 calories per day. Teen boys need about 2700 to 2800 calories. Naturally, these numbers vary according to height, build, and level of activity. The bigger you are, and the more active you are, the more calories you need just to maintain your body weight.

The more active you are, the higher your **basal metabolic rate**. The basal metabolic rate is the rate at which you use the energy from food for automatic body processes like breathing. Some people have a higher basal metabolic rate than others. They can eat a lot without gaining weight. You can speed up your basal metabolic rate by increasing the amount of physical

---

activity that you do. This will help you to lose weight. When you get older, you will have to eat less or increase your activity level in order to keep your weight the same. The basal metabolic rate decreases with age.

The Right Weight

How much should you weigh? According to most health experts, an adult woman should weigh 100 pounds for the first five feet and five additional pounds for each extra inch of height. This formula says that you should add ten pounds to the total if you have a large frame. You should subtract ten pounds for a small frame. That means that an adult woman of five feet six inches should weigh 130 pounds. Of course, these figures are for adults. Teens usually weigh less, since their bodies are still developing.

An adult male should weigh 106 pounds for the first five feet and six additional pounds for each inch above five feet. Again, add or subtract ten pounds for a large or small frame.

Weight Chart for Adult Males			
Height	Small Frame	Average Frame	Large Frame
5'0"	96 pounds	106 pounds	116 pounds
5'1"	102 pounds	112 pounds	122 pounds
5'2"	108 pounds	118 pounds	128 pounds
5'3"	114 pounds	124 pounds	134 pounds
5'4"	120 pounds	130 pounds	140 pounds
5'5"	126 pounds	136 pounds	146 pounds
5'6"	132 pounds	142 pounds	152 pounds
5'7"	138 pounds	148 pounds	158 pounds
5'8"	144 pounds	154 pounds	164 pounds

Counting Calories

Suppose you want to lose weight. You must eat 3500 calories less than you normally use just to lose one pound. That is not so hard to do. Just eat 500 calories less than you need per day. After one week you will be one pound lighter. In six months, you will have lost 25 pounds. By the same arithmetic, if you are underweight, you can gain weight by adding 500 calories per day to your diet.

Cutting out sweets is a quick way of eliminating calories. Skip the jelly doughnut (225 calories), the cheese Danish (375 calories), and the candy bar (300 calories). Instead have a slice of cantaloupe (45 calories), an apple (85 calories), or half a cup of ice milk (93 calories).

Food preparation is also a factor in weight reduction. A baked potato is only 75 calories. Adding two teaspoons of butter brings the calorie count up to 140. A fresh peach is only 65 calories. Two canned peach halves in heavy syrup are 160 calories.

Dairy products	Measure	Calories
Cheese, cheddar	1 oz.	115
Cheese, cottage, small curd	1 cup	220
Cheese, cream	1 oz.	100
Cheese, Swiss	1 oz.	105
Cheese. pasteurized process, American	1 oz.	82
Half-and-half	1 tbsp.	20
Cream, sour	1 tbsp.	25
Milk, whole	1 cup	150
Milk, nonfat (skim)	1 cup	85
Eggs		
Fried in butter	1	85
Hard cooked	1	80
Scrambled in butter (milk added)	1	95
Fats & oils		
Butter	1 tbsp.	100
Margarine	1 tbsp.	100
Meat, poultry, fish		
Bluefish, baked w/butter or margarine	3 oz.	135
Clams, raw meat only	3 oz.	65
Crabmeat, white or king, canned	1 cup	135
Fish sticks, breaded, cooked, frozen	1 oz.	50
Salmon, pink, canned	3 oz.	120
Sardines, Atlantic, canned in oil	3 oz.	175

Calories in Certain Foods

Dieting

Sensible dieting is the way to go. Crash diets take weight off more quickly, but the pounds usually come right back. That is because you are not changing your eating habits when you crash diet. Then, when you go back to your normal eating patterns, you are still eating the same foods that made you overweight in the first place. What you need to do is change your whole way of eating. Then, when you stop dieting, you will still be eating nutritious, but lower calorie, foods.

A pattern of gaining and losing weight makes permanent weight loss extremely difficult. A very low calorie diet tells your body that it is not getting enough food. To protect itself from starvation, the body lowers its basal metabolic rate. With a lower basal metabolic rate, you do not burn up as many calories as usual. When you stop dieting, your metabolic rate remains low. You gain more weight because your body does not use calories as fast as it did before your diet.

Anorexia Nervosa

Some young people, especially women, are so concerned with weight loss that they become ill. Although they are very thin, they believe they are too fat. They think that every ounce of flesh on their bodies is disgusting and must be eliminated. This disease is **anorexia nervosa**. Anorexics fool their families. They push their food around on their plates, but rarely eat. They excuse themselves from family meals by claiming that they have already eaten. They make themselves vomit to get rid of food still in their stomachs. Before anyone realizes what is happening, the anorexic gets so thin that they must be hospitalized and fed through a tube. Unfortunately, some victims of this disease die before they can get medical help.

Bulimia

Bulimia is another disease associated with dieting. Bulimics often eat enormous amounts of food. They eat gallons of ice cream and whole packages of cookies and cake. Then they make themselves vomit. Bulimia is a continuous cycle of binge eating and vomiting. Both bulimics and anorexics need psychological help to dealwith their problems.

Physical Activity

How does physical activity help your body? You already know that exercise helps keep your weight down. Exercise helps in other ways, too. Exercise tones muscles, strengthens bones, helps decrease fat in blood  vessels, improves the condition of your heart muscles, gets more oxygen into your body, and makes you more flexible. Exercise also helps you to fall asleep and makes it easier for you to deal with stress. Working out or participating in a sport makes you feel better about yourself. In fact, some psychologists believe that a brisk one-mile walk may help to combat depression.

Starting a regular exercise program can help you look better. Your muscles will be in tone. Your skin will look better. You will have more energy to do the things you want to do.

Isn't it worth the effort?

What Is Physical Fitness?

Physical fitness involves having enough energy to do the things that you want to do. There are many aspects of physical fitness. Muscular strength and endurance, flexibility, cardiovascular fitness, and a lean body composition are the basis for physical fitness.

Muscular strength is the amount of force that your muscles exert to overcome a resistance. Muscular strength enables you to lift, bend, push, and pull. With greater muscular strength, you can lift heavier objects or do harder jobs. Doing specific exercises while working out at a gym will strengthen your muscles. For example, push-ups strengthen the biceps, the muscles of the upper arm. A planned, supervised program of exercise can lead to improved muscular strength.

Muscular endurance lets you use your muscles for longer periods of time. Muscular endurance helps you to perform better as an athlete. The more you practice in appropriate ways at a sport, the more endurance your muscles will have. Each sports activity requires the use of specific sets of muscles. For example, swimming relies on a different set of muscles from the ones you use in baseball or basketball.

Flexibility is the ability to twist, turn, bend, and stretch easily. Flexibility means good joint movement without injuries. Stretching improves flexibility. So do dancing, gymnastics, and bending. In general, any activity improves flexibility.

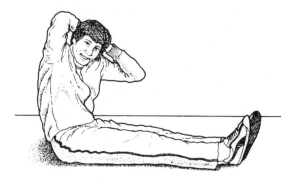

Cardiovascular fitness means the ability of the heart and blood vessels to transport blood carrying oxygen to the cells. Aerobic means using air or oxygen. So cardiovascular fitness is also called aerobic fitness. **Aerobic exercises** are any exercises that improve cardiovascular fitness. Aerobic exercises strengthen the heart muscles so that they become more efficient. An efficient heart can pump more blood without beating faster. Walking, jogging, swimming, cross-country skiing, biking, and dancing are all good aerobic exercises. In order to improve cardiovascular fitness, you should exercise three or four times per week for at least twenty minutes per session.

Lean body composition means that the amount of fat in the body is low compared to the amount of muscle. Females have about 23 percent body fat. Males have about 17 percent. Your body type and heredity are related to how much fat you have.

CHECK YOUR UNDERSTANDING

1. Define the term *calorie*.
2. Describe a basal metabolic rate.
3. How many calories do you have to eliminate in order to lose one pound?
4. Why don't crash diets work?
5. What is anorexia nervosa?
6. Write a definition of physical fitness.
7. How will weight-lifting improve your body?
8. What exercises improve flexibility?
9. Why is cardiovascular fitness so important?
10. What factors determine the percent of fat in your body?

KEY IDEA #3:
Taking care of your teeth, skin, and hair improves
your appearance and prevents disease.

It's Up to You

You can improve the condition of your teeth, skin, and hair. By doing so, you will improve your health and your appearance. You will feel and look better. Sometimes it will not be easy. Sometimes you will feel like giving up. But, caring for yourself will pay off in good appearance and good health.

About the Teeth

Your teeth have a lot to do with your ap-pearance. This seems strange, because only a small part of each tooth, the outer layer, can be seen. This layer is made of **enamel,** the hardest material made by the body. It is the only part of the tooth that is not living matter.

Underneath the enamel is the living part of the tooth. It contains blood vessels and nerves. This part continues into the gums and is attached to the jawbone by strong roots. This living part of the tooth resembles a tree, planted in the ground.

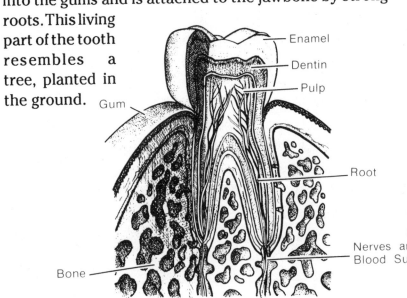

A Tooth

As babies grow, they soon get twenty teeth. These are the primary, or baby, teeth. At about age six, baby teeth begin to fall out. They are replaced by permanent teeth. As the years go by, additional teeth appear in the mouth.

Adults have thirty-two permanent teeth, with different teeth for different jobs. The front and side teeth cut and tear food. The back teeth, or **molars**, grind food. The molars in the very back of the mouth are the last ones to appear. These molars are the **wisdom teeth**. Most people get their wisdom teeth between the ages of 18 and 21. Sometimes wisdom teeth appear much later.

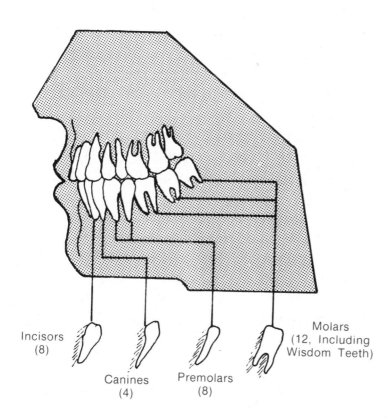

Incisors
(8)

Canines
(4)

Premolars
(8)

Molars
(12, Including
Wisdom Teeth)

Problems of the Teeth and Gums

The dental problem that worries most people is **cavities**. Cavities are holes in the teeth caused by tooth decay. **Plaque** causes tooth decay. Plaque is a combination of sugar, saliva, and bacteria. The bacteria act on the sugar to form acid. The acid causes tooth decay unless it is removed by brushing. Cavities need to be filled when they are small. If not, the entire tooth can decay.

Some wisdom teeth cause problems. They come in crooked or cause pain when they break through the gums. Impacted wisdom teeth press against the other molars. Some dentists recommend pulling impacted teeth before they do any damage.

The major dental problem that affects adults over age 40 is **periodontal disease**. Periodontal disease begins with plaque. If it is not removed, the plaque turns into a hard substance called tartar. Tartar pushes against the gums and forms pockets between the gums and teeth. The gums become red and swollen, and begin to bleed. The pockets collect pus, food, and more plaque. Eventually, the gums pull away from the teeth. The teeth become loose and may fall out.

Malocclusion is improper bite. That means the upper and lower teeth do not come together as they should. Malocclusion sometimes causes speech problems and can affect appearance. **Braces** are appliances used to change the position of the teeth and straighten them. **Orthodontists** are dentists who specialize in correcting malocclusion.

Preventive Tooth Care

Preventive care actually prevents or stops something from happening. Preventive tooth care prevents tooth and gum disease from happening. A good diet, fluorides, proper cleaning, and dental checkups are the preventive measures that stop tooth and gum disease.

A good diet is the first step. Too many sweets cause bacteria in the mouth to multiply. This encourages tooth decay and can lead to gum disease. You should avoid eating too many sweets. **Fluoride** is a chemical substance that reduces tooth decay. Fluoride is added to water in most cities. Some dentists also give fluoride treatments to children. Most toothpastes contain fluoride.

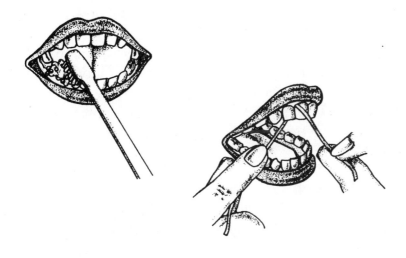

Brushing and flossing reduce tooth decay and help prevent gum disease. Brush your teeth after meals, if possible, since bacteria begin to grow right after eating. Floss your teeth before you go to bed. **Flossing** means inserting dental floss between the teeth and moving it back and forth in order to get the food out. A toothbrush cannot fit between the teeth. Dental floss can. Dental floss looks like sewing thread. It is either plain or coated with wax. Most dentists advise the use of unwaxed dental floss. If you find unwaxed floss difficult to use, start out with the waxed version.

Regular dental visits are important. A professional cleaning removes tartar from the teeth before it causes periodontal disease. Dentists are able to find small cavities and fill them before the entire tooth decays. Dentists take x-rays to locate cavities. X-rays are special photographs that show the insides of the teeth. Too many x-rays are dangerous, so dentists do not take them at every visit.

About the Skin

The skin is an organ, just like the heart or lungs. In fact, it is the largest organ in the human body. The skin has many functions. It is a sense organ with touch receptors for heat, cold, and pain. It is a giant cover that keeps the air from drying up the moist inner systems. The skin keeps the body cool by producing perspiration. It protects the other organs from injury. It is a screen against bacteria. Your skin also protects you from the sun's rays.

The Epidermis

There are two main layers of the skin. They are the **epidermis**, or outer layer, and the **dermis**, or inner layer. The epidermis is composed of cells. New cells are made all the time in the lower part of the epidermis. Older cells are pushed up toward the top of the skin. When they reach the surface, they are dead. The dead cells flake off on towels and clothing.

Pores, or tiny openings, are located in the epidermis. Pores are connected to the sweat glands. **Melanin** is also manufactured in the epidermis. Melanin gives your skin its color. It protects you against the ultraviolet rays of the sun. When you remain in the sun too long, the skin produces an overabundance of melanin. This is how some people get a tan. Some people also get freckles from the sun. Freckles are small patches of melanin.

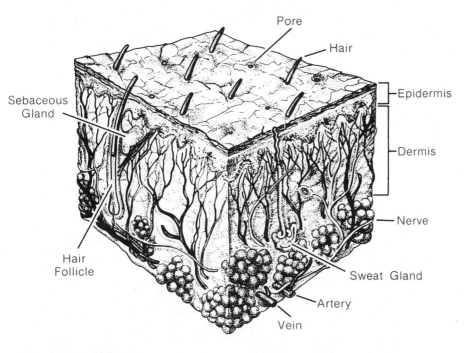

Pore

Hair

Epidermis

Dermis

Sebaceous
Gland

Nerve

Hair
Follicle

Sweat Gland

Artery

Vein

The Dermis

The dermis contains the blood vessels, nerves, and glands. Oil glands secrete a material called **sebum**. Sebum is an oily substance that lubricates the body. Too much sebum can clog up the pores and cause pimples and blackheads. Sweat glands secrete perspiration. Perspiration contains water, salt, and other waste materials. The sweat glands under the arms and in other hairy places on the body produce a fatty kind of sweat. When this sweat comes in contact with the bacteria on the skin, an unpleasant odor is produced. Washing with soap and water decreases odor by reducing the growth of bacteria. Deodorants can counteract these odors. Antiperspirants fight this problem by closing the pores.

The lower layer of the dermis contains fatty tissue. It insulates the body from heat and cold and protects it from injury.

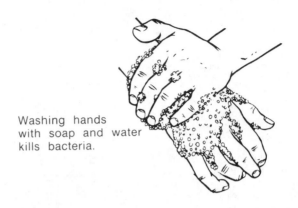

Washing hands with soap and water kills bacteria.

Skin Disorders

Skin disorders are a big problem during the teen years. Medical researchers have realized this. They have developed many new ways of treating these problems.

Acne

Acne is the most common skin disorder of teens. Adolescence is a time when hormones cause the glands to produce more oil. Acne is a combination of pimples, blackheads, and cysts. Acne affects the face. It is also found on the neck, shoulders, and back. A blackhead is a clogged pore. When bacteria enter the clogged pore, it becomes infected. White blood cells act to kill the bacteria. The clogged pore turns yellow-white. This is a pimple. A cyst results when a deeper area of the skin is infected.

Acne can be treated in many ways. Wash your face often with soap and water to get rid of dirt and oil. Use a lotion containing sulfur, resorcinol, or benzoyl peroxide. These nonprescription products dry the skin and cause it to peel. Avoid oily creams or cosmetics. Wash off all makeup before going to bed. If nothing works, see a **dermatologist**. A dermatologist is a doctor who treats skin disorders. Dermatologists can prescribe antibiotics or stronger lotions. Retinoid compounds have been found effective in treating severe acne. However, they have serious side effects and should be used only under the care and direction of a physician.

Other Skin Problems

Sunburn causes more problems than most people think. Besides pain and redness, fever and chills may occur. But these are only temporary disorders. The long-term effects of the sun are much worse. The chances that you will get skin cancer are directly related to the amount of time spent in the sun. Farmers and fishermen, for example, are more likely to have skin cancer. In addition, frequent exposure to the sun causes wrinkling of the skin. Many suntan products contain PABA, a chemical that blocks out the sun. The PABA content of a suntan preparation can range from 1 (almost no sunblock) to 22 (a complete sunblock). These products reduce the damage caused by the sun.

Allergies are the reactions of the body to a particular substance. Many people are allergic to poison ivy and poison oak. The oils from these plants cause a reaction in the skin. Small blisters appear. The skin becomes red and itchy. **Hives** are red, raised areas on the skin. Hives are allergic reactions to many substances, including foods and medicines.

Poison Ivy

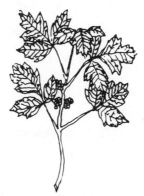

Poison Oak

Moles look like bumps on the skin. They are not a problem if they remain the same. If they change in size or color, a doctor should check and possibly remove them. Dark, changing moles can develop into cancer.

Itching and cracking between the toes may mean **athlete's foot**. Athlete's foot is caused by a **fungus**. A fungus is an organism that grows in moist places, such as a locker room floor. To prevent athlete's foot, keep your feet dry. If you develop this disorder, you can cure it by using a nonprescription powder or cream that was specifically developed for this.

Care of the Hair

Hair is made of transparent cells that lie flat and reflect the light. This is what makes your hair shine. When dirt attaches itself to the hair shaft, light cannot be reflected very well. The hair becomes dull and dingy. Shampooing and brushing remove dirt and grime. Brushing the hair also distributes scalp oil. This also makes hair shiny. Excessive blow drying, permanent waving, or hair coloring can cause hair to become dry and brittle. Hot oil treatments or conditioners can help hair look and feel better.

Hair Problems

Many people are bothered by **dandruff**. Dandruff is a condition in which the outer cells of the scalp flake off. Frequent shampooing and brushing usually eliminate dandruff. If they do not, you might need to use a special shampoo. If you have red, oozing patches on the scalp in addition to the flakes, you might have a condition more serious than dandruff. In that case, you need to see a doctor.

Ringworm is a skin condition that produces balding and itchy patches in the scalp. It is transmitted from one person to another by sharing hats and combs. Ringworm is caused by a fungus that grows in damp places, such as the floor of a shower or locker room. Washing and drying the hair thoroughly can prevent ringworm.

Head lice are insects that suck blood from the scalp. They travel from one person to another on hats and combs and through body contact. Head lice thrive in schools. They infect people by laying eggs in their scalps. The eggs are called nits.

If your scalp is itchy or irritated, you might have head lice. Ask the school nurse or someone that you know to check your scalp for lice and nits. Nits are small, light-colored eggs. Although they are very tiny, nits are easier to spot than lice because there are more of them. A magnifying glass might be necessary.

You can kill head lice by washing your hair with a special shampoo. These shampoos kill lice but not nits. Use a fine-toothed comb to get the nits out. Shampoo again in about a week. You don't need a prescription for these shampoos. Just ask a druggist for the name of any of the special shampoos that kill head lice. These non-prescription shampoos are safe and effective as long as the instructions are followed exactly.

CHECK YOUR UNDERSTANDING

1. What are molars?
2. Why do wisdom teeth cause problems?
3. What is periodontal disease?
4. List four things that you can do to prevent tooth and gum disease.
5. List three functions of the skin.
6. Name the two main layers of the skin.
7. How do soap and water reduce body odor?
8. List three ways of treating acne.
9. Why is a locker room floor a likely place to pick up athlete's foot?
10. How do you get rid of head lice?

Summary of Chapter 8

Nutrition means nourishing the body with the nutrients in foods. The six basic nutrients are carbohydrates, proteins, fats, vitamins, minerals, and water. Food can be divided into four major groups: the milk group, the meat group, the vegetable-fruit group, and the bread-cereal group. In order to get all the nutrients you need, eat foods from all four food groups.

Basal metabolic rate is the rate it takes to use the energy from food to keep your heart beating and your body functioning. The more active you are, the higher your basal metabolic rate will be. You will also use more calories. If you cut out 500 calories each day, you will lose one pound at the end of a week.

Physical fitness means having enough energy to do the things you want to do. There are many aspects of physical fitness. These include muscular strength and endurance, flexibility, cardiovascular fitness, and lean body composition.

You can improve your looks and prevent disease by taking care of your teeth, skin, and hair. To have good teeth, avoid sweets, brush and floss each day, use flouride toothpaste or get fluoride treatments, and have regular dental checkups. Preventive tooth care can reduce your chances of getting cavities and periodontal disease. Acne is the most common skin problem of teens. To treat acne, wash your face often and use drying lotions. See a dermatologist if necessary. Other skin problems include sunburn, moles, and athlete's foot. Washing the hair will keep it clean and shiny. Special soaps can effectively treat dandruff and head lice.

WORDS TO USE

1. nutrition	27. lean body composition
2. nutrients	28. enamel
3. carbohydrate	29. molars
4. glucose	30. wisdom teeth
5. cellulose	31. cavities
6. constipation	32. plaque
7. proteins	33. wisdom teeth
8. amino acids	34. periodontal disease
9. essential amino acids	35. malocclusion
10. fats	36. fluoride
11. cholesterol	37. flossing
12. saturated fats	38. epidermis
13. polyunsaturated fats	39. dermis
14. vitamins	40. pores
15. minerals	41. melanin
16. sodium	42. sebum
17. calcium	43. acne
18. osteoporosis	44. dermatologist
19. calorie	45. allergies
20. basal metabolic rate	46. hives
21. anorexia nervosa	47. moles
22. bulimia	48. athlete's foot
23. physical fitness	49. fungus
24. flexibility	50. dandruff
25. cardiovascular fitness	51. ringworm
26. aerobic exercises	52. head lice

REVIEW QUESTIONS FOR CHAPTER 8

1. Why do cells need nutrients?
2. What is the most healthful way to get carbohydrates in your diet?
3. How can you get complete proteins without eating animal products?
4. How can you prevent cholesterol buildup?
5. Name three polyunsaturated fats.
6. How will a lack of vitamin C affect the body?
7. What does potassium do for the body?
8. How can knowing the four basic food groups help you get the nutrients you need?
9. How can you speed up your basal metabolic rate?
10. Name some desserts that are low in calories.
11. What are two eating disorders?
12. How does physical activity help your body?
13. What does flexibility mean?
14. Why are aerobic exercises so important?
15. How many teeth does an adult usually have?
16. Why should cavities be filled when they are small?
17. What is malocclusion?
18. What are the three ways of getting the fluoride that your teeth need?
19. What are pores?
20. What happens when the oil glands produce too much sebum?
21. Why is sunburn harmful to the skin?
22. Why can moles be dangerous?
23. What makes the hair shine?
24. How do head lice travel from person to person?

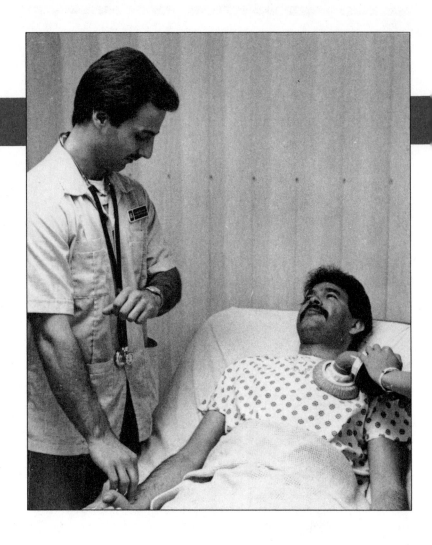

CHAPTER GOAL:

To understand that both heredity and environment play a part in the transmission of diseases.

KEY IDEAS:

Infectious diseases are caused by pathogens and are spread from one organism to another.

Chronic diseases such as cardiovascular diseases and cancer develop because of hereditary and environmental factors.

The Nature of Disease

KEY IDEA #1:
Infectious diseases are caused by pathogens and are spread from one organism to another.

Pathogens

In the fourteenth century, more than half the people in Europe caught the bubonic plague. Because this disease killed so many people, it was named the Black Death. Today, the common cold affects a large number of people. A cold makes you feel miserable, but once it is gone you feel fine again—quite different from the Black Death!

Yet, the plague and the cold have much in common. They are both caused by **pathogens**, or disease-causing organisms. They are both passed from one person to another. They are both infectious diseases.

Infectious Diseases

Infectious diseases are diseases that are passed from one organism to another. People infect each other by sneezing or coughing or through body contact. Germs are also spread in polluted drinking water. Infectious diseases are called **communicable diseases** because they are spread from one person to another.

At one time, the cause of disease was a mystery. People thought that evil spirits were to blame. Then, in the nineteenth century, a French scientist named Louis Pasteur formulated the **germ theory** of disease. The germ theory claims that germs are the cause of disease. What are germs? How do they get around to do so much damage?

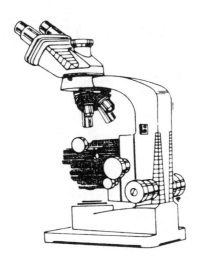

Microbes

Germs are so small that they cannot be seen with the naked eye. These pathogens are only visible under a microscope. For this reason, they are called **microorganisms** or **microbes**. You have probably heard of bacterial or viral infections. Perhaps you have had one of these illnesses yourself. **Bacteria** and **viruses** are two kinds of microbes. Not all microbes are harmful. But the pathogens, the harmful ones, can cause many kinds of infectious diseases.

Microbes can be carried from place to place by rats, pigs, mosquitoes, flies, and fleas. They are then transmitted to humans. Microbes can be found all over. They live in water, in waste materials, and in the coughs and sneezes of sick people. But if microbes are everywhere, why are we not sick all the time?

Your Defense Against Microbes

The body has a defense system that guards against microbes. Structures of the body form the first line of defense. The skin prevents most germs from entering the body. The mucus in the nose and throat traps the microbes until they are coughed or sneezed out. The tonsils and the acids in the stomach also help to destroy microbes. If germs do get inside the body, the second line of defense takes over. An army of white blood cells surrounds and captures the germs at the place of infection.

The **immune system** is the final line of defense. When a foreign substance enters the bloodstream, the blood makes **antibodies**. Antibodies are proteins that kill specific microbes. Some antibodies remain in the body after a disease is over. These antibodies prevent you from getting the disease again. You then have an **immunity** to that particular disease.

Without your immune system you would die of an infection. There are some babies who are born without a normally functioning immune system. Perhaps you have seen pictures of the child who had to live in a germ-free bubble. A bone marrow transplant can sometimes restore normal immunity, since white blood cells are made in the bone marrow.

In the early 1980s, a newly-found disease called **AIDS** (acquired immune deficiency syndrome) was reported. AIDS is an immune system disease. The patient cannot fight infections. He or she becomes weak and dies. AIDS is caused by a virus and is transmitted by sexual contact, by the use of contaminated intravenous needles, or by blood transfusions. Since the mid-1980s, however, blood donation centers have taken steps to assure a safe blood supply. Blood donors are screened, and blood is routinely tested for antibodies to the AIDS virus. There is presently no cure for AIDS.

Immunity

Some immunities are inborn. For example, humans cannot get certain diseases that animals get. Humans are naturally immune to such diseases.

Some immunities are acquired naturally. Babies are protected from certain diseases because of antibodies in their mother's milk. People can become immune to a disease after being exposed to it. This immunity lasts for a very long time, perhaps a lifetime. Once you have mumps, for example, you will probably not catch the disease again.

A **vaccine** provides an artificial immunity to a disease. A vaccine is a serum of weakened or dead microbes. When injected with a vaccine, the body manufactures antibodies against that disease. The patient might feel ill for a while, but a short-term sick feeling is better than a serious disease.

The Smallpox Vaccination

In the early 1800s, smallpox was the killer disease of the time. Edward Jenner, an English physician, developed a vaccine for this disease. Jenner observed that milkmaids often got a mild disease called cowpox, but never caught smallpox. He thought that if he introduced a small amount of cowpox into a person's body, that vaccine from cowpox would make a person immune to smallpox.

Jenner put material from a cowpox sore into the arm of a young boy. The boy developed cowpox and recovered. Next, Jenner inoculated the boy with smallpox material. The boy did not get smallpox at all. His body had produced antibodies against smallpox which made him immune to the disease.

Today there are vaccinations for many infectious diseases, including mumps, measles, German measles, diphtheria, pertussis, tetanus, and polio.

Antibiotics

Infectious diseases can be treated with **antibiotics**. Antibiotics are chemicals made from living organisms. There are many antibiotics in use today, but the first one was penicillin. Penicillin is made from a mold. It was discovered by Sir Alexander Fleming, a Scottish scientist.

Antibiotics can only be used to treat bacterial infections. There is still no treatment for a viral illness. However, scientists are working with chemicals called **interferons**. Interferons are chemical messengers that tell cells what to do. Scientists have produced artificial interferon in the laboratory. They are trying to get interferon to tell the cells to produce antiviral chemicals. An antiviral chemical could kill a virus.

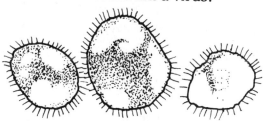

Flu viruses, magnified about 200,000 times.

Sanitation

Sanitation is also responsible for preventing disease from spreading. Sanitation is the process of making things free from filth and infectious matter. Sanitation makes things hygienic and clean. At one time, waste products in cesspools and rivers contaminated drinking water with bacteria and viruses. There were epidemics of typhoid fever and cholera. Thousands of people died. Before the germ theory was known and germs were understood as a cause of sickness and death, many people died while in the hospital. Doctors did not always wash their hands between operations, so germs were passed from one patient to another. Hospital rooms were not sanitized, so pathogens multiplied wildly.

Today, the water you drink is filtered and purified before it ever reaches your house. Government agencies test the water to be sure it is safe to drink. Government agencies also control the safety of food and medicines in our stores. Strict rules of sanitation are observed in hospitals. Physicians not only wash their hands, but scrub them with special materials to get rid of all germs. Operating rooms are also scrubbed, and sanitary clothing and draperies are used for all hospital personnel and patients.

Yet, with all the precautions taken today, much still needs to be done. Although the United States and most developed countries have clean drinking water, many countries in the world do not. These countries are still troubled by diseases like smallpox and typhoid fever. In addition, all nations, including the United States, still must be on guard against harmful practices such as dumping chemical wastes into rivers and contaminating drinking water in other ways.

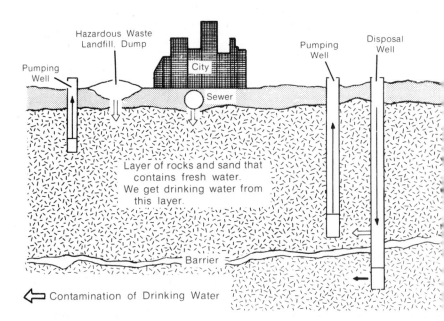

Infectious Diseases Today

The common cold, influenza (the flu), and pneumonia are three of the most common infectious diseases that are still with us today. Although the flu is not serious for most people, it can be deadly for certain members of the population, especially the elderly and those people suffering from heart and lung diseases. Influenza weakens the body and leaves it open to more serious infections, such as pneumonia.

Sexually transmitted diseases (STDs) are also with us today. In fact, the incidence of STDs has been rising. STDs are diseases that are transmitted through sexual contact. People with many sexual partners are at great risk of getting these diseases.

CHECK YOUR UNDERSTANDING

1. What are infectious diseases?
2. Name two types of microbes.
3. How do microorganisms get from one place to another?
4. What are the body's three types of defenses against germs?
5. What are antibodies?
6. What would happen if your immune system did not work?
7. What is a vaccine?
8. What does an antibiotic do?
9. Why is good sanitation so important?

Today's Health Problems

At one time, most people died from communicable diseases which spread from one person to another. Vaccines, antibiotics, and improved sanitation have eliminated or brought under control most communicable diseases from the United States and other developed countries. Today, the major killers in these countries are cardiovascular diseases and cancer.

Noncommunicable Diseases

Heart disease and cancer are **noncommunicable diseases**. Noncommunicable diseases are not spread from one person to another. They are not caused by pathogens. Instead, they are caused by problems inside the body. These diseases can be **chronic diseases**, because they affect people over a long period of time. But what causes chronic diseases to develop?

Heredity

Chromosomes are tiny, rod-shaped bodies located in the nucleus of each cell. Chromosomes carry hereditary information. You get half your chromosomes from your mother and half from your father.

Examples of pairs of chromosomes of a human male

Genes are located on the chromosomes. There are genes for every trait in an organism. Your genes give you your skin color, your body structure, and your other physical traits. Your genes can be the cause of certain inheritable diseases. Your genes can also make it more likely for you to develop other diseases.

Genetic Diseases

If two parents have the same gene for a certain disease, they can pass this disease on to their children. **Diabetes** seems to run in families. People with diabetes have an abnormal amount of sugar in their bodies. Diabetics must eliminate sugar from their diets. They can take a drug called insulin to lower the amount of sugar in their blood. Some diabetics control their sugar level by diet alone. Others take prescribed dosages of medicines.

Sickle-cell anemia is a genetic disorder which affects the red blood cells. It causes weakness and irregular heart action. Sickle-cell anemia affects eight to ten percent of the black population of the United States. At present, there is no known cure for this disease.

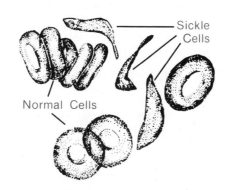

Sickle Cells

Normal Cells

The Effects of Environment

Drugs, alcohol, smoking, and poor nutrition have a harmful effect on an individual. These same factors can affect an unborn child. Babies born to mothers who smoke have a lower birth weight than babies born to nonsmoking mothers. Babies of drug addicts are addicts themselves when they are born. X-rays and leakage from nuclear reactors can also damage an unborn child by causing changes in the genes.

Cardiovascular Diseases

Cardiovascular diseases are also called heart diseases. These are disorders that affect the heart and blood vessels. You might have heard that heart disease runs in families. This is true to some extent because of the traits that you inherit from your parents. However, environmental factors are also responsible for cardiovascular diseases. In other words, what you do with your life can increase or decrease your likelihood of getting heart disease.

Smoking, being overweight, not exercising, and eating too much fat in the diet are all factors that contribute to heart disease. Chapter 4, The Circulatory System, tells more about cardiovascular diseases.

Cancer

Cancer is a disease in which there is an abnormal and uncontrolled growth of cells. It is normal for cells in the body to divide and produce new cells. However, when cells divide abnormally and grow too rapidly, a lump is formed. This mass of tissue is called a **tumor**. Most tumors are **benign**. That is, they are not harmful. Benign tumors are noncancerous. However, some tumors are **malignant**. Malignant tumors are cancerous and may cause death.

Like heart disease, cancer seems to run in families. However, the way you treat your body can also increase or decrease your likelihood of getting cancer. Smoking is a cause of lung cancer, for example. Tobacco contains **carcinogens,** or cancer-causing substances. Carcinogens sometimes develop from x-rays, ultraviolet radiation, and food additives. A high-fat, low-fiber diet seems to contribute to cancer of the colon and rectum. Excessive exposure to the sun can cause skin cancer.

Early detection and treatment of cancer are the best ways of increasing the chance of survival. Some cancers, if found early enough, can be treated before spreading throughout the body. What are some of the signs of cancer? The American Cancer Society has a list of seven warning signals. If you notice one of these signs, it does not mean that you have cancer. It does mean that you should see a doctor to be sure that nothing is wrong.

Cancer's Seven Warning Signals
1. **C**hange in bowel or bladder habits
2. **A** sore that does not heal
3. **U**nusual bleeding or discharge
4. **T**hickening or lump in breast or elsewhere
5. **I**ndigestion or difficulty in swallowing
6. **O**bvious change in wart or mole
7. **N**agging cough or hoarseness

Types of Cancer

Although cancers can be found in any part of the body, there are some places where they seem to occur more frequently. Lung cancer is one such cancer. At one time, lung cancer was found mostly in men. As more and more women began to smoke, they also got this disease. Most lung cancers could be prevented if people did not smoke. The warnings printed on each pack of cigarettes are meant to demonstrate the effect of smoking and its dangers.

Breast cancer is the most common cancer of women over 50 years of age. Women should check their breasts every month for lumps. A special type of x-ray called a **mammogram** can detect cancer of the breast at a very early stage. Doctors recommend that women between the ages of 35 and 40 have a baseline mammogram and women between 40 and 50 have one done every two years. They recommend that women over 50 have a mammogram every year. Cervical cancer used to be one of the most frequent causes of death in women. Now, a simple test called a **Pap smear** can detect cervical cancer at a very early stage. A Pap smear is a painless procedure. The doctor takes some cells from the cervix and examines them in a laboratory. Women over the age of 20 should have a Pap smear every year.

Leukemia is the most common kind of cancer in children. Leukemia is cancer of the blood. There are many treatments for leukemia today.

Treatment for Cancer

The three main methods of treating cancer are surgery, radiation therapy, and chemotherapy. Surgery is used to remove cancers that are confined to small areas of the body. In **radiation therapy,** radiation is aimed at cancer cells in order to kill them. **Chemotherapy** is the treatment of cancer with certain drugs. Chemotherapy has some serious side effects, such as loss of hair or nausea. However, it has proved to be a useful tool in treating cancer.

CHECK YOUR UNDERSTANDING

1. What are chronic diseases?
2. What are chromosomes?
3. Name two genetic diseases.
4. How can the environment affect an unborn child?
5. Name some factors that contribute to heart diseases.
6. What is the difference between a benign tumor and a malignant tumor?
7. List three of cancer's warning signals.
8. How can lung cancer be prevented?
9. List three ways of treating cancer.

Summary of Chapter 9

Infectious diseases are caused by germs. Germs or pathogens are usually so small that they can only be seen with a microscope. These microbes can be either bacterial or viral. The body has three lines of defense against microbes: the skin and other body structures, the white blood cells, and the immune system. The immune system makes antibodies that kill germs. Some immunities are inborn, some are acquired naturally, and some are produced by vaccines. Vaccinations, antibiotics, and sanitation have decreased the incidence of infectious diseases.

Today, most people die from chronic diseases such as cancer or cardiovascular diseases. Chronic diseases can run in families. Chromosomes carry hereditary information from parents to children. There are genes on the chromosomes for every trait of an organism. For this reason, genetic diseases can be passed from one generation to the next. Environmental factors can increase or decrease your chance of contracting a chronic disease.

Cardiovascular diseases affect the heart and blood vessels. Smoking, being overweight, not getting enough exercise, and eating too much fat in the diet all contribute to heart disease. Cancer is a disease in which there is an abnormal and uncontrolled growth of cells. Uncontrolled cell growth results in a tumor. A tumor can be either benign or malignant. Some cancers are preventable. For example, not smoking can prevent lung cancer. Early detection of cancer increases the survival rate. The American Cancer Society lists seven warning signals for cancer. Surgery, radiation therapy, and chemotherapy are three ways of treating cancer.

WORDS TO USE

1. pathogens
2. infectious diseases
3. communicable diseases
4. germ theory
5. microorganisms
6. microbes
7. bacteria
8. viruses
9. immune system
10. antibodies
11. immunity
12. AIDS
13. vaccine
14. antibiotics
15. interferons
16. sanitation
17. noncommunicable diseases
18. chronic diseases
19. chromosomes
20. genes
21. diabetes
22. sickle-cell anemia
23. cardiovascular diseases
24. cancer
25. tumor
26. benign
27. malignant
28. carcinogens
29. mammogram
30. Pap smear
31. leukemia
32. radiation therapy
33. chemotherapy

REVIEW QUESTIONS FOR CHAPTER 9

1. How are the plague and the common cold alike?
2. What is the difference between communicable and noncommunicable diseases?
3. What is the germ theory?
4. How does the immune system guard against disease?
5. When Edward Jenner injected a boy with smallpox, why did the boy not get the disease?
6. What are interferons?
7. How do hospitals try to prevent the spread of germs?
8. What are genes?
9. What parts of the body do cardiovascular diseases affect?
10. What is the difference between cancer cells and normal cells?
11. What are some ways of preventing cancer?
12. Why is it important to detect and treat cancer early?
13. What is chemotherapy?

CHAPTER GOALS:

To identify and describe some drugs that are widely used today.

To explain why drug abuse is harmful.

To create an awareness of the dangers of drug use.

To encourage students to avoid drugs.

KEY IDEAS:

The drug habit causes physical and psychological damage to the body. Once begun, it is difficult to stop.

Alcohol is a drug that causes physical, emotional, and social damage.

Tobacco is harmful to the body. It is especially hazardous to the respiratory and cardiovascular systems.

10

Drugs, Alcohol, and Tobacco

KEY IDEA #1:
The drug habit causes physical and psychological damage to the body. Once begun, it is difficult to stop.

Using and Abusing Drugs

A drug is a chemical substance taken into the body that changes the normal pattern of work for the mind or body. Not all drugs are bad. Some are very useful. Antibiotics and insulin are useful drugs. Without antibiotics, people could die of infections. Without regular shots of insulin, people with diabetes would die. Physicians prescribe antibiotics and other **prescription drugs** for certain illnesses. Prescription drugs can only be obtained with a prescription or order signed by a doctor. Aspirin and cough medicine are **over-the-counter drugs** used to relieve headaches and coughs. They may be purchased without a prescription. Many useful prescription and over-the-counter drugs are available.

It is only when drugs are misused or abused that they are dangerous. People who buy and use "street drugs," such as heroin or LSD, are abusing drugs. They are harming their bodies. They also are breaking the law. People who take a pill for every occasion are misusing drugs. They may be called drug abusers. Dangers from prescription drugs result from their improper use.

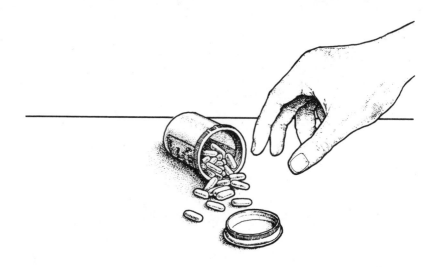

Dependence on Drugs

If you take a drug over a period of time, you may become dependent on that drug. This dependence is called **drug addiction**. Your body actually develops a need for the drug. As time goes by, your body may need more and more of the drug in order to get the same feeling or effect that you got when you first took the drug. This need is called **physical addiction**. If you are physically addicted to a drug and stop taking it, you can develop withdrawal symptoms. You might have stomach pains, chills, a fever, or difficulty breathing.

Even if a drug does not cause a physical addiction, you may grow to depend on it emotionally. This is called a **psychological addiction**. Often, physical and psychological addictions are developed at the same time.

Stimulants

Drugs can be either stimulants or depressants. Some people call stimulants "uppers." They also call depressants "downers." **Stimulants** increase the activity of the central nervous system. They speed up the heart rate and raise blood pressure. They pep you up and make you more alert. People take stimulants when they are depressed or when they just want to "feel high." They also take them when they want to stay awake or lose weight.

One of the most common stimulants is **caffeine**. Caffeine is found in coffee, tea, chocolate, and soft drinks. Caffeine, like the other stimulants, increases activity in the central nervous system. As a result, coffee drinkers are wide awake. Caffeine is not without dangers. Caffeine increases the rate of the heartbeat and raises the blood pressure. Some people become extremely nervous from too much caffeine.

Cocaine is another stimulant that speeds up the activity of the central nervous system. In large amounts, cocaine can cause hallucinations, or strange visions. "Crack" is a highly addictive form of cocaine. Many young people have been experimenting with crack just to see what it is like. They are finding themselves addicted to the drug after a very short time.

Marijuana is one of the most common street drugs. It is often called "grass." Marijuana does not have the same effect on all people. It can cause a loss of memory, a feeling of confusion, or a sense of being out of your own body. For this reason, it is not safe to drive when you are under the influence of marijuana.

Marijuana Leaf

Depressants

Depressants work on the body by slowing it down. For this reason, people who take depressants are often sleepy, or seem to be in a daze. Many users take depressants to help them forget their troubles. Little do they realize that the depressant itself will be the cause of their biggest troubles.

Narcotic Depressants

Morphine and **heroin** are two drugs made from the opium plant. They are both depressants. They are also narcotics. Narcotics are drugs that cause physical addiction. They are powerful drugs that affect the central nervous system. Narcotics provide brief feelings of pleasure or lightness. They are especially dangerous because their use makes it easy to form the drug habit.

Morphine is used as a medicine to relieve pain. Without morphine, many surgical procedures could not be performed. Patients would not be able to withstand the pain of certain illnesses.

Heroin is a "street drug." It is extremely habit-forming. It causes both physical and psychological addiction.

Other Depressants

Tranquilizers, barbiturates, hallucinogens, PCP, and inhalants are all nonnarcotic depressants. Although they are not physically addicting, they are emotionally habit-forming. When you stop using a nonnarcotic drug, you will not have the painful withdrawal symptoms that you get from a narcotic like heroin. It will still be difficult to stop, though, because you are used to the feeling that you get from the drug.

Barbiturates are sleeping pills. **Tranquilizers** are drugs that calm you down. Barbiturates and tranquilizers are drugs that doctors prescribe to treat anxiety and depression. People often use barbiturates and tranquilizers as a crutch. They become so dependent on these prescription drugs that they cannot function without them. Some doctors are guilty of prescribing these drugs for too long a period of time. Most doctors will not do this. They feel that these drugs should be used to help a patient over a crisis, but not on a long-term basis.

Hallucinogens give people **hallucinations**, or weird visions. Two common hallucinogens are LSD and mescaline. Phencyclidine, also called PCP or angel dust, can also cause hallucinations. In addition, PCP can change a person's behavior to such an extent that a once calm person becomes violent.

Inhalants include gasoline, kerosene, model glue, and paint thinner. These substances are called inhalants because they are inhaled into the body through the lungs. Inhalants are very dangerous. They can cause permanent liver damage, unconsciousness, and death.

Why Start?

You may know some people who are in trouble because of drugs. Think about how some famous entertainers and sports figures have overdosed and died. People who work with drug users say that it is very difficult for the addict to get off drugs. Some of them want to quit, but they cannot.

The smart thing is not to start. Say "No!" to drugs. If you do that, you will save yourself the personal pain drug abuse brings. Remember, it is your decision, your brain, and your body. Decide for yourself what you want to put into your body. Do not let others decide for you.

How Can You Stop?

What if you are already on drugs? What if you have a friend or family member who is a drug user? You need somebody to talk with. Talk to a teacher or counselor at school; a minister, rabbi, or priest; a friend or relative; a doctor or nurse. Most areas have special drug centers where drug abusers can go for treatment or advice. A drug hotline is also useful. A **drug hotline** is a special, no-charge telephone number that anyone can call. You can use it to talk to a trained person about a drug problem. This person will tell you what to do next, or where you can go for help. **Alcoholics Anonymous (AA)** is an organization for the treatment of alcoholism. You can attend an AA meeting or call an AA office. It is not just for alcoholics, though. People who abuse any other kinds of drugs go to AA meetings for help.

Sometimes you want to quit, but you cannot do it all by yourself. Seeking outside help may solve this problem.

CHECK YOUR UNDERSTANDING

1. Explain the statement, "Not all drugs are bad."
2. What is a physical addiction?
3. Tell the difference between a stimulant and a depressant.
4. Name two stimulants and two depressants.
5. What is "crack"? Why is it so dangerous?
6. What is a barbiturate?
7. Why are inhalants so harmful?
8. What are two ways that drug abusers can help themselves to get off drugs?

KEY IDEA #2:
Alcohol is a drug that causes physical, emotional,
and social damage.

The Drug Called Alcohol

A drug is a nonfood substance that changes the way the mind or body usually works. Alcohol enters the bloodstream quickly. It causes body functions to slow down. For this reason, alcohol is a drug. In fact, alcohol is the drug used most often in the United States. Alcoholism is one of the most widespread diseases in our society. Alcoholism affects not only the alcoholic, but the alcoholic's family, friends, and society in general.

Types of Alcohol

There are many kinds of alcohol. Denatured alcohol is used for industrial purposes. Isopropyl alcohol is rubbing alcohol. Methanol is found in paint thinners, turpentine, and similar products. These forms of alcohol are very poisonous. The kind of alcohol found in beverages is ethanol.

How Alcoholic Beverages Are Made

There are two major processes for making alcoholic beverages. They are called fermentation and distillation. In fermentation, yeast is used to convert sugar to alcohol. Yeast plants are tiny fungi that cause chemical changes in sugar. Wine is made by fermenting grapes. Beer is made by fermenting barley. Wine has an alcohol content of about eight to fifteen percent. Beer contains about three to six percent alcohol. In the process of distillation, alcohol is heated and cooled to make stronger liquor. Distillation produces "hard" liquor, or liquor with an alcohol content of forty to sixty percent.

1 ounce of whisky   3 ounces of wine   12 ounces of beer

These drinks contain about the same amount of alcohol.

Alcohol and Your Body

Although wine and beer contain less alcohol than hard liquor, people generally drink more of these beverages. So, a person who is drinking wine or beer may actually consume the same amount of alcohol as someone who is drinking scotch or rye. A jigger of hard liquor, a glass of wine, and a can of beer all contain about the same amount of alcohol.

When a person drinks an alcoholic beverage, most of the alcohol is quickly absorbed into the bloodstream. A small amount is excreted through the kidneys and lungs. That is why you can smell alcohol on the breath of a person who has been drinking. The alcohol that is not excreted must be oxidized by the liver. In the process of oxidation, the liver changes the alcohol to carbon dioxide and water. It takes about one hour for the liver to oxidize one ounce of alcohol. That means that it takes an hour for the alcohol in an average drink to leave the bloodstream.

The Blood Alcohol Level

The amount of alcohol in the blood is called the **blood alcohol level**, or BAL. The BAL can be measured with an instrument called a breathalyzer. In the breathalyzer test, you blow into a bag that is attached to a machine. The machine reads out the amount of alcohol in your blood. Police officers use the breathalyzer to determine whether drivers are legally **intoxicated**, or drunk. In most states, a person with a blood alcohol level of 0.10 percent is considered to be intoxicated. Drunken drivers can have their licenses suspended. A person who is convicted of driving while intoxicated receives a jail sentence and a steep fine.

Your blood alcohol level depends on other factors besides the number of drinks that you have had. Some people oxidize alcohol at a faster rate than others. Also, the more you weigh, the more alcohol your body can oxidize. If two people drink the same amount of alcohol, the person who weighs 120 pounds will have a higher blood alcohol level than the person who weighs 190 pounds. Eating also slows down the effects of alcohol. If your stomach contains food, it will take longer for the alcohol to reach your bloodstream.

Although a BAL of 0.10 percent is considered too high for safe driving, any amount of alcohol in the bloodstream impairs your ability to drive. Even one drink can slow down your system. You do not think and respond as quickly as you normally would. The amount of time that it takes for you to respond or react to a situation is called your reaction time. While driving, competing in sports, or using machines like power tools, it is important to react quickly. Since alcohol is a depressant, it slows down your reaction time.

What Alcohol Does

Alcohol is the most widely used depressant. Like other depressant drugs, alcohol slows down the activity of the central nervous system. At first, alcohol acts as a stimulant. If you continue drinking, alcohol acts as a depressant. It slurs your speech, makes walking difficult, affects your vision, and clouds your judgment.

The chart below shows how many drinks it takes to raise your blood alcohol level, according to your weight. Look at the chart. Suppose that you weighed 140 pounds. After four drinks, your BAL would be 0.11 percent. In most states, you would be legally drunk. You should not be driving an automobile. How many drinks would it take to make you legally intoxicated if you weighed 100 pounds?

Blood Alcohol Level (BAL) in Percent

Number of Drinks	Weight in Pounds							
	100	120	140	160	180	200	220	240
1	.04	.03	.03	.02	.02	.02	.02	.02
2	.08	.06	.05	.05	.04	.04	.03	.03
3	.11	.09	.08	.07	.06	.06	.05	.05
4	.15	.12	.11	.09	.08	.08	.07	.06
5	.19	.16	.13	.12	.11	.09	.09	.08
6	.23	.19	.16	.14	.13	.11	.10	.09
7	.26	.22	.19	.15	.15	.13	.12	.11
8	.30	.25	.21	.19	.17	.15	.14	.13
9	.34	.28	.24	.21	.19	.17	.15	.14
10	.38	.31	.27	.23	.21	.19	.17	.17

The second chart, "How Alcohol Affects You," shows what happens as more and more alcohol gets into your bloodstream. Suppose that you weigh 140 pounds and have a BAL of 0.08 percent. According to the chart, you would not be functioning very well either physically or mentally. Your speech would be slurred, and you would have difficulty walking. If you took just one more drink, your BAL would be 0.11 percent. You would not be able to make responsible decisions and, in most states, you would be considered to be legally intoxicated.

How Alcohol Affects You

Blood Alcohol Level	What the Alcohol Does to You
.02	You feel relaxed and easygoing.
.06	Both your mind and body are affected. You have trouble walking, and your speech is slurred.
.10	Your mind is not clear, and you cannot make responsible decisions. In most states, you are considered to be intoxicated.
.12	You have difficulty seeing and speaking clearly. You may feel sick and vomit.
.15	You will act abnormally and fall asleep.
.30	You will be in a deep sleep.
.50	You will be in a coma and might die.

Why People Drink

Drinking and driving do not mix. Drinking and schoolwork do not go together, either. Neither do drinking and athletics. Drinking affects a person's ability to make good judgments. It often leads to fights and accidents. Then why do so many people drink?

People say they drink to feel good, to have a good time. They say drinking helps them forget their problems. They think it makes life more enjoyable. These people may consider themselves social drinkers. Some of them may actually be problem drinkers.

Alcoholism

You probably know many people who drink alcoholic beverages. They might be your friends and relatives. Many do not have drinking problems. But some of them are **alcoholics**. Alcoholics are people who cannot control their drinking. They are not able to have just one or two drinks. They have to keep on drinking. Alcoholics have a disease called **alcoholism**.

Why do people become alcoholics? Suppose a person has a problem. He might take a drink or two each day. The drinks make the person forget the problem. Suppose the problem does not go away. After a while, a drink or two is not enough to help forget the problem. Now, it takes three or four drinks. The drinker has developed a **tolerance** for alcohol. It takes more and more alcohol to get the same good feeling.

A tolerance for alcohol can lead to alcoholism. In alcoholism, there is both a physical and a psychological need to drink. When alcoholics cannot get a drink, they develop withdrawal symptoms, the way heroin addicts do. They may have chills and fever and hallucinations. Getting a drink becomes the all-important issue.

People may have a tendency toward alcoholism, in the same way that they have a tendency toward heart disease or cancer. As with other diseases, alcoholism seems to run in families. Scientists are beginning to think that the chemistry of the body and a tolerance for alcohol are the forerunners of alcoholism. If you have a parent or close relative who is an alcoholic, then you have good reason to be careful about drinking.

Should You Drink?

The decision is up to you. If you are reading this book in a school classroom, you are probably under twenty-one years of age. In that case, drinking is probably against the law for you. In most states, you can be arrested if found with alcohol in your possession. What about later on, though? You might decide that you never want to drink. Perhaps you know people who have wrecked their life or the life of others because of alcohol. Maybe you don't want to put any drugs into your body.

Some people never drink. They may not like the taste of alcohol. Drinking may be against their religion. They may not be able to drink because of a medical problem. They may have decided that alcohol is harmful.

It is up to you to decide whether to allow alcohol to affect your mind and your body. Your **peers**, or people of your own age and social group, should not make that decision for you. A friend may ask you to have a drink, but that does not mean that you have to say yes. You can "SAY NO TO DRUGS."

Is Alcohol Really Bad for You?

Even small amounts of alcohol affect your mind and body. Because alcohol clouds your mind, you have difficulty making decisions. Normal people often act very strange after having a few drinks. They take chances and do things that they ordinarily would never do. They say things that they are sorry for later. They get into fights. Since alcohol affects coordination, it can lead to injuries and accidents. People who drink are more likely to die from fires and falls.

Alcohol is responsible for half of all traffic accidents. Drunken driving is a serious problem, both for the driver and the innocent victims. There are organizations that were formed for the purpose of getting drunken drivers off the road. One organization is called Mothers Against Drunk Drivers, or MADD. It was formed by a group of women whose children had been killed by drunken drivers. A student group, Students Against Drunk Drivers, or SADD, has been organized. Both organizations want stiffer penalties for drunken drivers. The members want these drivers off the roads and in jail.

Excessive drinking can damage the liver. The liver is the organ that oxidizes alcohol. Heavy drinking causes a liver disease called **cirrhosis**. In cirrhosis, normal liver tissue is destroyed and replaced by scar tissue. Cirrhosis is a serious disease that can result in death. Excess alcohol also causes nutritional deficiencies. Alcoholics seldom care about eating well. Their poor diets can lead to other disorders.

Alcohol is also dangerous for unborn babies. Pregnant women who are heavy drinkers have a greater chance of giving birth to babies with physical and mental defects. These babies are the victims of **fetal alcohol syndrome**. This syndrome affects the babies of women who have more than six drinks a day. Even two drinks a day during pregnancy can damage an unborn child. Studies show that mothers who have two drinks a day have a greater risk of miscarriage. Their babies are usually smaller than normal. There is a chance that they will have learning disabilities. However, doctors are not sure about the effects of any amount of alcohol on an unborn child. For this reason, pregnant women are advised not to drink at all.

Even occasional excessive drinking can cause problems. Do you know what a **hangover** is? If you do, then you know that the nausea and vomiting, the extreme thirst, and the pounding headache of a hangover are not any fun. A hangover is the body's way of recovering from too much alcohol. Your body is telling you that you have had too much to drink.

Are You a Problem Drinker?

Do you have a drinking problem? Are you worried about becoming an alcoholic? Are you concerned about someone else? Take this quiz. If you answer "yes" to any of these questions, you may need to change your behavior. If you are thinking of somebody else when you read the questions, just substitute the person's name whenever you see the word you.

1. Do you drink more than your friends?
2. Do you have to drink more than you used to in order to get the same effect?
3. Do you drink when you have a problem?

4. Do you have to drink in order to feel good?

5. Is alcohol usually part of your social life?

6. Have you ever gotten into trouble because of drinking?

7. Have you ever missed school because of drinking?

8. Do you ever drink alone?

9. If you decided to stop drinking, would it be difficult to do so?

How Can You Get Help?

If you have a problem with alcohol, or if you know someone else who has a problem, you should deal with it right away. Do not put it in the back of your mind, hoping that it will go away. Talk to your parents if you can. Speak to a teacher or counselor at school. If you attend church or synagogue, see your priest, minister, or rabbi.

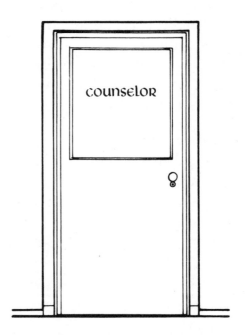

If no one that you know can help you or if you prefer to talk to someone who does not know you at all, contact Alcoholics Anonymous (AA). AA is a national organization for the treatment of alcoholism. It has chapters in almost every city and town in the United States. AA is a self-help group. Members encourage each other to avoid alcohol. Meetings are held seven days a week. Anyone is welcome to attend. Those attending use their first names only. Anything said at a meeting is kept confidential by other members. Al-Anon and Alateen are two groups that help family members learn to deal with the problems of living with an alcoholic. People from ages twelve to twenty can join Alateen.

CHECK YOUR UNDERSTANDING

1. Why is alcohol classified as a drug?
2. When you drink an alcoholic beverage, where does most of the alcohol go after it enters the body?
3. Which organ oxidizes alcohol?
4. What is meant by the term blood alcohol level?
5. How does alcohol affect your reaction time?
6. If you weigh 160 pounds and have four drinks, what would your BAL be?
7. How would you act if you had a BAL of 0.06 percent?
8. What is an alcoholic?
9. What is cirrhosis of the liver?
10. What is fetal alcohol syndrome?
11. What are two signs of a drinking problem?
12. How can alcoholics help themselves to stop drinking?

Why Smoke?

When you ask people why they smoke, you get many different answers. "It's relaxing," or "It makes me feel good," or "Lots of people smoke." Whatever the answer, it is the wrong answer. Nothing good comes from smoking.

Tobacco Is a Drug

Within the tobacco plant is a substance called nicotine. Nicotine is a drug, a nonfood substance, that alters the mind or body in some way. **Nicotine** is a stimulant. It speeds up the activity in the central nervous system. It makes you feel alert. That's why heavy smokers may act jumpy or nervous.

Tobacco Is Harmful to the Body

If you were to eat the nicotine in one cigar, you would probably die. Since nicotine is chewed or inhaled, instead of being eaten, it takes longer for the damage to take place. There is damage, though. Experiments have shown that when mice take in cigarette smoke the way human smokers do, they have convulsions and die. Smoking is a cause of lung cancer and a contributing factor in heart disease.

How Smoking Affects the Respiratory System

In an earlier chapter, you studied the respiratory system. You learned that air enters the body through the nose and continues down the trachea. The trachea divides into two branches called bronchi. Each branch goes into one of the lungs. Inside the lungs, the bronchi divide into smaller and smaller tubes. The bronchi and their branches are called bronchial tubes. Bronchioles are the smallest of these tubes. They connect to tiny sacs that are known as alveoli. People who smoke have more disorders of the bronchial tubes, alveoli, and lungs than nonsmokers do. Smokers are more likely to develop chronic bronchitis, emphysema, and lung cancer.

Chronic Bronchitis

Bronchitis is an inflammation of the lining of the airways. It usually follows a cold or the flu and produces a cough. Smokers are more likely to develop **chronic bronchitis**. This condition lasts for several months. It may recur year after year. People call chronic bronchitis "smoker's cough."

Emphysema

In **emphysema**, the alveoli are destroyed over a period of time. People who have this condition become short of breath. They have difficulty performing the simplest tasks. In order to get enough oxygen into their lungs, they have to inhale it from an oxygen tank. Many people, especially those who are heavy smokers, die from emphysema.

Lung Cancer

Lung cancer is a disease in which the cells of the lungs multiply abnormally, causing a growth or tumor in the lungs. Smoking is responsible for the majority of lung cancers. Cigarette smoke contains **tar,** a sticky substance made up of many chemicals. It is the tar in cigarette smoke that is largely responsible for lung cancer. X-rays of the chest and lungs can reveal cancer.

Unfortunately, by the time the cancer is discovered, it is usually too late. Most lung cancer victims are dead within five years after they learn about the disease. Even if the cancer is discovered early, fewer than half of the people survive. Research into cures and treatment continues.

Smoking Affects the Cardiovascular System

The cardiovascular system includes the heart and the blood vessels. Smoking can lead to cardiovascular diseases.

When tobacco is burned, **carbon monoxide** gas is released. Carbon monoxide is found in the exhaust of automobiles, too. It is a deadly gas. Running a car inside a closed garage produces carbon monoxide that can kill a person. People who smoke cigarettes are also inhaling this deadly gas into their lungs. The surgeon general of the United States warns of this danger with a label printed on every package of cigarettes.

When carbon monoxide from tobacco smoke gets into the body, it causes a decrease in the amount of oxygen in the blood cells. As a result, body tissues are deprived of oxygen. Over a period of time, this lack of oxygen is harmful to the heart and the blood vessels. In addition, the nicotine in cigarettes speeds up the heart rate and causes the blood pressure to increase. This makes the cardiovascular system work harder. The combination of nicotine and carbon monoxide puts an unnecessary strain on the cardiovascular system. This leads to heart disease.

Other Effects of Tobacco

Women who smoke are more likely to miscarry when pregnant. If they do give birth, their babies are usually smaller than normal. Smaller babies are less likely to survive to be healthy adults. It follows that pregnant women should avoid tobacco.

Smokers are more likely to develop cancer of the larynx, mouth, and esophagus. Perhaps you have seen a person speak by holding a small device in front of his or her throat. This kind of device is used by someone whose cancerous larynx has been removed. Without a larynx, a person cannot speak in the normal way.

Tobacco smoke even affects nonsmokers. The smoke that people inhale from their own cigarettes is called mainstream smoke. Smoke from ashtrays or from other people's cigarettes is called secondhand smoke. Studies show that secondhand smoke is harmful to nonsmokers. Is it any wonder that every package of cigarettes contains some warning of the dangers involved?

Cigars, Pipes, and Chewing Tobacco

So far, you have been reading about cigarettes. What about pipes and cigars? Pipe and cigar smokers are not as likely to get heart and lung disease, because they usually do not inhale. However, former cigarette smokers who switch to pipes and cigars continue to inhale. They run an even greater risk of cardiovascular and respiratory disorders. Also, pipe and cigar smokers are more likely to develop cancer of the lips and mouth. Chewing tobacco is also dangerous. Although you don't smoke it, you do keep it inside your cheek. This increases the chance of developing cancer of the mouth.

Anything Else?

Think of how tobacco wrecks your looks. It discolors your teeth, stains your fingers, and makes your breath smell horrible. Nonsmokers say that kissing a smoker is like kissing a stale ashtray. Recent studies show that tobacco smoke causes the skin around the mouth to wrinkle.

What About Low-Tar Cigarettes?

You might think that low-tar cigarettes are the answer. Unfortunately, they are not. Smokers who switch to cigarettes with reduced tar and nicotine usually smoke more and inhale more deeply. They are not really lowering their tar and nicotine intake at all.

Stopping the Habit

If you do smoke, you probably have not been smoking for many years. If you stop now, you will reduce your risk of getting cancer, heart disease, or any of the other illnesses associated with tobacco. If you are a smoker, your lungs are gray. After you stop smoking for a few years, they will be pink and healthy once more. Even people who have been smoking for twenty years can benefit from quitting. After one year without tobacco, a former smoker's risk of developing heart disease drops sharply. After ten years without tobacco, the risk is the same as for someone who has never smoked.

Naturally, it takes willpower to kick the cigarette habit. Nicotine is a drug with addictive powers. After a while, both your mind and your body become dependent on tobacco. Some people attend special clinics to help them stop smoking. Others substitute something else for tobacco. They may jog around the block or shoot some baskets whenever they have the urge to smoke. Whichever way you quit, it is worth it. Nobody has ever found anything good in cigarettes.

If You Do Not Smoke

If you have never smoked, you certainly should not start now. Do not change your mind. Do not let your friends influence you. Even if you are the only one in your crowd who does not smoke, be strong. You will probably avoid lung cancer and emphysema, as well as many other problems smoking brings.

1. Why is tobacco considered a drug?
2. Define chronic bronchitis.
3. What is the substance in tobacco smoke that causes lung cancer?
4. How does carbon monoxide contribute to heart disease?
5. Why is it dangerous for pregnant women to smoke?
6. What type of cancer can chewing tobacco cause?
7. What is the difference between mainstream smoke and secondhand smoke?
8. Why is it difficult to stop smoking?

Summary of Chapter 10

A drug is any nonfood substance that changes the mind or body. Drugs taken as medicine help to cure disease. Drugs used for other reasons are harmful. Drugs are classified as stimulants or depressants. Stimulants increase activity in the central nervous system. Depressants slow down body processes.

Drugs are habit-forming. They can cause psychological or physical addiction. Narcotics cause a physical dependence. Over a period of time, larger and larger doses are needed. When the narcotic is discontinued, painful withdrawal symptoms occur.

Alcohol and tobacco are drugs. Alcohol is responsible for half of all traffic accidents. Tobacco causes cancer and contributes to heart disease. Other drugs produce hallucinations, dizziness, and even death.

WORDS TO USE

1. *prescription drugs*
2. *over-the-counter drugs*
3. *drug addiction*
4. *physical addiction*
5. *psychological addiction*
6. *stimulants*
7. *caffeine*
8. *cocaine*
9. *marijuana*
10. *depressants*
11. *narcotics*
12. *morphine*
13. *heroin*
14. *barbiturates*
15. *tranquilizers*
16. *hallucinations*
17. *inhalants*
18. *drug hotline*
19. *blood alcohol level*
20. *intoxicated*
21. *alcoholics*
22. *alcoholism*
23. *tolerance*
24. *peers*
25. *cirrhosis*
26. *Fetal Alcohol Syndrome*
27. *hangover*
28. *nicotine*
29. *chronic bronchitis*
30. *emphysema*
31. *lung cancer*
32. *tar*
33. *carbon monoxide*

REVIEW QUESTIONS FOR CHAPTER 10

1. What is an over-the-counter drug?
2. Define the term *narcotic*.
3. What is the difference between physical and psychological addiction?
4. How do depressants affect the body?
5. Why is morphine a useful drug?
6. Why are barbiturates and tranquilizers misused?
7. What is a drug hotline?
8. Define the term *drug*.
9. What would happen if you drank methanol?
10. What does a breathalyzer test measure?
11. What is intoxication?
12. List three reasons why the same amount of alcoho makes one person drunker than another.
13. What would your blood alcohol level be if you weighed 140 pounds and had four drinks?
14. How would a blood alcohol level of 0.30 percent affect your body?
15. Explain what a "tolerance for alcohol" means.
16. What is SADD?
17. What are the symptoms of a hangover?
18. List three signs of a problem drinker.
19. What do the initials AA stand for?
20. How does tobacco affect the respiratory system?
21. What is emphysema?
22. Why is lung cancer such a serious disease?
23. How does carbon monoxide affect the blood cells?
24. How does the color of a person's lungs change after he gives up smoking?
25. What are the dangers of smoking pipes and cigars?

CHAPTER GOALS:

To recognize that there are many aspects of mental and emotional health.

To describe the nature of stress and recognize ways of coping with tension.

KEY IDEAS;

Both heredity and environment play a part in mental and emotional health. They set behavior patterns.

The way in which people deal with their feelings has an influence on their health, or wellness.

Defense mechanisms are behaviors used to relieve and avoid conflicts.

Emotional problems and mental disorders require treatment or therapy.

CHAPTER 11

Mental and Emotional Health

KEY IDEA #1:
Both heredity and environment play a part in mental and emotional health. They set behavior patterns.

The Brain and Behavior

Why do humans act the way they do? What causes people to confide in their friends, or withdraw in unfriendly situations? These reactions are called **human behavior**. Your behavior is controlled by your body and your mind. It is also shaped, to some extent, by the actions of people around you.

It is hard to learn about behavior because behavior is so dependent on the brain. It is much easier to learn about other body systems than it is to learn about the mind and how it works. The human brain is one of the most amazing structures in existence. It stores countless bits of information and uses them rapidly to respond to any situation. Studying what the brain does is both puzzling and interesting. Scientists have not yet explained the total range of the brain's work and its effect on human behavior.

Biological Versus Mental

Human behavior is a mix of body and mind. Behavior combines biological activity, or body actions, and mental activity, or actions of the mind, or brain.

Sometimes, one part of the formula is more important than the other. For example, if you break your leg, the physical pain controls your actions. The body is in charge.

On the other hand, there are situations where the mind controls behavior. Imagine that you have just failed a mathematics test for the third time this semester. The news spells trouble for you. You become anxious. You may never have had a problem like this before. You may not be able to think about anything else. These are all mental processes. Your body is not directly involved.

Your body gives you some signals, though. You may have sweaty hands, a headache, or an upset stomach. But these physical reactions are not controlling your behavior. The mental activity caused by failing a mathematics test is affecting your behavior.

Behavior Is a Balance

In human behavior, many things happen at the same time. But the roots of the behavior are in the structure and function of cell materials. This is **biological**. This cell action does not account for all behavior, however. Sometimes, it seems that the body is just a stage for the mind to act out its roles. Both mental and biological activities are equally important in determining how a person behaves.

Heredity Affects Behavior

Heredity has to do with the traits you inherit from your parents. You may have noticed that some of your friends look and behave just like one of their parents. A boy or girl whose appearance and behavior resemble one parent is sometimes called "a chip off the old block." This is one way of saying that **heredity** plays a part in causing behavior. Inherited traits are passed on through the **chromosomes.**

These chromosomes are in the nucleus, or center, of every cell. The set of chromosomes that each individual has came from the material in the egg and sperm that formed them. Behavior traits controlled by genes often run in families.

Behavior and Environment

Your surroundings, or **environment**, also affect behavior. When you are young, your behavior patterns are centered around your relationship with your parents. Later, your behavior centers around relationships with your friends and classmates. It is influenced by the things you do, the books you read, the jobs you take, and many other factors that make up your environment. You may have heard the saying, "No two individuals are alike." Your environment and your chromosomes work together to make that true.

CHECK YOUR UNDERSTANDING

1. Why is it hard to learn about human behavior?
2. What part of behavior can be described as biological?
3. What is the meaning of the phrase, "A chip off the old block"?
4. What part do chromosomes play in heredity?

The way in which people deal with their feelings has an influence on their health, or wellness.

Emotions and Behavior

The basic **emotions** are love, anger, and fear. Emotions involve feelings. These feelings range from pleasure to pain and anguish. Individuals experience a wide range of emotions.

Not everyone shows the same emotions. For example, some people seem never to get angry. Others seem to be angry all the time.

Emotions determine some part of your life-style. Your emotions can lead the way in approaching different situations. Avoiding emotional pain and seeking emotional pleasure are active parts of a person's life-style. Your behavior patterns can be a mirror reflection of your emotions.

Emotions

Are you aware of your own emotions? Emotions are feelings, such as love, joy, happiness, anger, fear, sadness, jealousy, rage, and satisfaction. Do you know what situations make you happy or afraid? Can you predict how you will feel if a certain event happens? Do you show your emotions, or hide them?

Mental Wellness

Emotional health, or wellness, depends on how people deal with their emotions. Sometimes, our emotional reactions are stretched to the limit. This creates a great problem. Dealing with the problem is important. Maintaining your mental wellness is as important as maintaining your physical wellness.

You constantly deal with different levels of emotions. You like this, or dislike that. One thing makes you happy, but another makes you very unhappy. Maintaining an even level of emotional responses is a true challenge. Because emotions are such a constant part of living, it is important to be aware of them. It is doubly important to be able to handle them. Dealing with the extremes that emotions can bring to your life is a measure of your emotional health.

The Force of Emotions

Emotions are a driving force. From infancy through old age, feelings stimulate behavior. You usually need different things at each stage of your life. But there are some basic emotional needs that never change. **Love** is one of these. It is a basic human emotion. People need love in order to have normal emotional health. Love takes different forms. It is shaped by different levels of intensity. But, in whatever shape or form, it focuses on the basic need for belonging.

The idea of relationships is central to the emotion of love. Relationships, whether with a friend or a family member, are built around emotions.

Self-Esteem

Emotions are the driving force in human relations. A driving force is something that makes the relationship work. In order to have relationships with others, you have to have good feelings for yourself. A feeling of **self-esteem**, or **self-worth**, is the emotion that drives a person to be responsible. The things you do at school, at home, at church, or at social events give you recognition. Getting recognition brings a feeling of self-esteem. It is natural to want recognition. It is natural to do things that will bring that recognition. Recognition brings about a feeling of self-worth. Having a good sense of self-worth is the starting point for good emotional and mental health.

Concern for others flows from a sense of self-worth. Knowing your own value allows you the freedom of speaking out for the rights and happiness of others, because you realize their value, also. Self-worth allows you to realize that it is better to give than receive. Self-worth leads you to satisfactory relationships with others. Because you can trust in yourself, you can trust in others. As you trust others, they will grow to trust you. This builds your feelings of self-worth. Through the driving force of the emotion of self-worth, you learn to have confidence in yourself. This confidence builds as you go through life.

Emotional Balance Builders

Whether you know it or not, each activity that you master can be an emotional balance builder. Each event that you consider to be a success can balance an event that you consider to be a failure. As you build your self-worth, you can add more and more emotional balance builders to your inventory.

Make a list of ten or fifteen things that have helped expand your feelings of self-worth. As you work on this list, you will continue to find things to add. Can you think of a reason why this happens?

An old adage says, "Success breeds success." When you discover that you have emotional balance builders, you are likely to discover even more of them. As you build your list, you are improving your mental health. You will soon hear someone say, "You certainly do have a good mental attitude!"

CHECK YOUR UNDERSTANDING

1. List the basic emotions.
2. Give the meaning of the term emotion.
3. What is one sign of emotional maturity?
4. What does the "the force of emotions" mean?
5. Describe how self-esteem plays a part in personal relationships.

KEY IDEA #3:
Defense mechanisms are behaviors used to relieve
and avoid conflicts.

Defensive Behavior

Defense mechanisms are kinds of behavior people use to avoid facing hard problems. They are used in a variety of situations. For people, problems involve **conflict**. Conflict causes an emotional tug-of-war. Nerves are on edge. People get tense and anxious. They call upon their favorite defense mechanisms. Instead of coping with the problem, they use these mechanisms to create a false solution to a real problem. It may seem to them that coming to the real solution is impossible.

For example, people hesitate to act when they are concerned that they might do the wrong thing. Instead of acting on the problem, they use a defense mechanism. Maybe they feel that they cannot figure out what is expected. Their behavior is **defensive.** The person is trying to protect his or her own feelings or beliefs. Most people use defense mechanisms at one time or another to help them cope with stress and anxiety.

Limited use of defense mechanisms is normal. But, when they are used over and over, they become excuses for not working directly on problems. When defense mechanisms are abused in this way, they can lead to serious emotional problems. Some of the more commonly used defense mechanisms like rationalization and daydreaming are described in this chapter. How many have you tried?

Rationalization

Rationalization involves making up excuses that do not fit a situation. For example, you may have wanted something very much. When you did not get it, you may have said, "Well, I did not want it anyway." You rationalized your loss. Almost everyone slips into this behavior on occasion. However, some people use rationalization as a way of life. They constantly provide people with believable but untrue reasons for the way they act.

Daydreaming

Another common defense mechanism is **daydreaming**. When you daydream, you place yourself in a make-believe world where you get to feel and act out anything your mind imagines. You can pretend that you are someone you would like to be, like a football hero or famous writer.

Brief encounters with this world of make-believe may be helpful—for a moment. If you daydream to the extreme, however, it can make real life pass you by. Daydreaming does not take the place of reality. It only lets you feel that way. Serious emotional and mental problems can develop when daydreaming becomes a way of life.

Negative Behavior

Turning to **negative behavior** because you are afraid that you are going to fail means always saying "No" to other people. People who use this defense mechanism do exactly the opposite of what might be suggested. Saying "Do not get into the cookies that I just baked" to a person who uses a negative behavior pattern is a signal for him or her to do the opposite. Being a negative person reduces conflict. Think about it. If you learn to say "No" to everything around you, people will not ask you to be involved. You reduce the risk of conflict by simply avoiding it. As in other defense mechanisms, the overuse of negative behavior can lead to serious mental and emotional problems.

Repression

Repression is another defense mechanism that occurs unconsciously. When you repress a problem, you escape it by not remembering it. In your mind, there is no problem. You can repress events that happened in the past.

Repression involves hidden behaviors and feelings. Sometimes they come to the surface. Then they cause stress and anxiety, particularly if they were unpleasant or difficult events. Continued repression as a regular behavior can lead to added anxiety and stress. Dealing openly with conflict as it happens seems to be the best way to maintain your mental health.

Regression

Regression is a defense mechanism that starts when a person is unable to work on a problem. When you regress, you use childlike behavior. People using this mechanism strike out at other people and objects that have no part in causing the problem. They behave as children do, looking to their mother and father to get them out of a bad situation. Sulking or throwing a tantrum are examples of regression. Regression calls attention away from the real conflict or problem. Regression prevents an individual from solving problems.

Denial

Denial is another defense mechanism. The main feature of denial is that a person denies reality. People who depend on drugs, alcohol, or tobacco without admitting they have a problem are using denial. By using denial, they avoid working on the solution to the problem. To them, there is no problem. They are avoiding conflict. But, they are trading the stress involved in solving the conflict for the stress involved in pretending that the problem does not exist.

CHECK YOUR UNDERSTANDING

1. What are defense mechanisms?
2. How can a defense mechanism be useful?
3. Give an example of rationalization.
4. Why is daydreaming a defense mechanism?
5. How does negative behavior work?
6. What types of events do people repress?
7. How does a person act who uses regression?
8. Give an example of how denial works as a defense mechanism.

Mental and Emotional Disorders

Almost everyone daydreams and uses other defensive behavior to help cope with problems. Some people, however, use behavior that is not normal and that interferes with regular daily life. These people need help to change the way they think and behave.

Phobias

Phobias are intense, irrational, unfounded fears. Phobias interfere with the normal activities of life. Although phobias are irrational, people with a phobia are really afraid. Fear of heights is one kind of phobia. Other phobias include fear of animals, thunderstorms, or the dark. Most people are aware of their phobias. They avoid the situations where the phobia may be called to mind.

A certain amount of fear is a healthy emotion. But, when the fear is based on some unreal or unlikely situation, it becomes an unhealthy fear. Fear of the dark is considered to be a phobia. It may have been learned as a child. But the fear is unfounded, because darkness does not harm you. When fear of the dark persists, it becomes a phobia.

Often, unfounded fears can be traced back to a situation that happened in the past. For example, as a child, you may have seen an adult who was frightened of thunderstorms. You learned that a thunderstorm was something to be afraid of. This feeling was intensified by the loud noise of the thunder and the flashes of lightning. Those very natural events become part of a fear pattern. Soon, you are violently afraid of thunderstorms. You have a phobia.

Guilt

When you experience **guilt**, there is a feeling of being anxious. For example, a problem may have developed and you feel responsible for causing it. You probably feel guilty when you break a rule at home or at school. This kind of guilt is not necessarily bad. It helps shape your overall value system. Because you do not like to feel guilty, you avoid breaking the rules.

The guilt that goes along with mental illness is not this kind of guilt. It is unrealistic guilt. Examples of this kind of reaction are feeling guilty that you were born, or believing that you are responsible for your parents getting a divorce. This unrealistic guilt can be a damaging feeling if you carry it too far. It can lead to serious feelings of shame and worthlessness.

You must learn to cope with guilt feelings. Everyone feels guilty about something at one time or another. But most people learn to handle these feelings. In order to do this, people have to realize that they cannot control everything. By setting reasonable goals for your behavior, doing the best that you can do in each situation, and recognizing that no one is perfect, you will be able to deal with guilt.

Depression

If feelings of guilt are carried to the extreme, they can lead to **depression**. Depression is a condition of sadness and dejection that lasts a period of time. It is one of the leading mental health problems of modern society. Most people have a good reason for feeling sad at certain times in their lives. The feeling usually goes away shortly. This is not the case with depression. People who are depressed show some signs of this mental disorder for months or even years. Some signs of depression are feeling sad, lacking interest, feeling inferior or tired, being moody, not being able to think clearly, and not being able to sleep well.

There is a big difference between feeling depressed for a day or two, and feeling depressed for a long period of time. Feeling depressed for a short time is very normal. But carrying these feelings for long periods of time is dangerous to your mental health. Depression can even lead to serious thoughts of suicide.

Mental health workers do not fully understand the causes of depression. Some believe that depression is rooted in chemical conditions in the body.

Generally, there is no one event that leads to feelings of depression. Sometimes, a serious loss, like the death of a family member, can set the stage. Other events are viewed through the sadness the death causes. That makes them seem more important than they really are. Everything that happens seems to be a catastrophe. The depression deepens. It lasts longer.

Your body can go through many reactions. You may lose your appetite. Your energy level may drop. People may feel that your personality has changed. You may even lose your direction about life and living. Not everyone who is depressed has all of these characteristics. But, depressed people usually have some of these characteristics for a long time.

Suicidal Behavior

Depression causes deep emotional concerns and conflicts. Sometimes, depression seems to be an impossible situation. Depressed people may even get the feeling that life has no value for them. In this state of mind, some people may talk of killing themselves. When somebody says that they are thinking of suicide, this is a danger sign. **Suicide** means intentionally taking your own life. Just talking about suicide may be a clue that a person is desperately reaching out for help. The thought of suicide may come and go very quickly, in response to feeling alone, overburdened with problems, or hopeless. However, there are times when these thoughts of suicide may linger. This causes a behavior pattern to develop where the possibility of suicide is more real.

There are some clues that are signs of an intention to commit suicide. Here is a list of them.

- Drastic changes in schoolwork.
- Increased and excessive use of alcohol.
- Erratic behavior, ranging from joyful one minute to extremely depressed the next.
- Increased smoking.
- Taking unnecessary risks; becoming a daredevil.
- Increased inability to make decisions.
- Withdrawal from friends, classmates, and family.
- Preoccupation with death in conversations.
- Writing poems or letters about death or dying.
- Loss of self-esteem.

Most people who think about suicide really do not want to die. They are probably in a difficult situation. For the moment, they can see no immediate solution to the problem. Sometimes, they have threatened to commit suicide before, or have even tried it. What can you do to help a person who feels this way?

If you hear someone talking about suicide, listen to what they have to say. A person who talks about suicide is calling out for help. Do not leave anyone in that state of mind. Be as helpful as you can be. Help the person think about other ways he or she might solve the problem. As you talk with the person, keep in mind that the threat to commit suicide is a serious one. Try to get help for the person. Ask him or her to go with you to a counselor, parents, doctor, or even to an emergency treatment room at the hospital. Help may be available by calling 911 or a suicide prevention center. Most important of all, let the person know that you really care.

People who attempt suicide require professional help. Emotional problems can be resolved with professional care and treatment. Many people who have attempted suicide go on to lead normal and happy lives.

When a person actually commits suicide, the person's friends and family may feel guilty. They may have tried their best to prevent the suicide. These friends and family must remember that the responsibility for choosing death over life is a personal one. The responsibility lies with the person who took his own life.

Seeking Help

Mental illness and emotional problems have a powerful effect on people's lives. The person with the problem is most affected. Family, relatives, and friends are also very much involved and influenced. The situation creates many problems for everyone involved. At times, these problems require the care of professionals who are trained to help people cope. These helpers include psychiatrists, psychologists, counselors, and social workers.

Psychotherapy

A psychiatrist can help a person who has a mental disorder. Discussing the situation that is causing a problem is the main treatment. The patient works with the therapist to seek out reasons for certain behaviors. Open discussions about feelings and thoughts lead to clearer understanding. This understanding can often eliminate the emotional problem or mental disorder. This is a basis of the treatment known as **psychotherapy**.

Group Therapy and Family Therapy

In addition to individual therapy, other kinds of therapy are available. **Group therapy** involves talk sessions among individuals with the same or similar problems. These discussions lead to clarifying and understanding individual behavior. The individuals in the group soon realize that they are not the only ones with a problem. Expressing opinions and sharing ideas about a common problem help the patient "see" the problem and learn how to handle it.

Basic Health

Family therapy is a special kind of group therapy. The family is a close-knit group. It can be the scene of great internal conflict. In family therapy, the therapist gets together with the entire family for group discussions. Each member of the family gets an opportunity to tell about his or her part in the problem situation. Common problems are discussed openly. Through clarifying and understanding harmful behavior, the family can begin to work on solving their problems. Together, they can see what they could not see as individuals. The issues that were never talked about are brought into the open. Family therapy can be the beginning of better attitudes and behaviors among all members of the family.

Drug Therapy

Drug therapy involves the use of medicine to treat mental or emotional disorders. The main methods of treatment are the use of tranquilizers and antidepressant drugs. These have to be prescribed by a **psychiatrist**. A psychiatrist is a medical doctor who has special training in dealing with mental and emotional problems. Drugs do not cure emotional problems, but they do give the therapist and patient a way of gaining control. Once some control has been gained, the therapist and patient can work on solving the problem or conflict.

Doctors prescribe tranquilizers to reduce tension and lessen anxiety. In more serious situations, tranquilizers can be used to treat patients who are hallucinating or having delusions. These people have lost touch with reality. They think they see things that really are not there.

Antidepressant drugs can elevate moods. They are used to make a person lose his feelings of depression.

Drug therapy is quite serious. It is reserved for patients who need the help of drugs to prepare for other kinds of therapy.

CHECK YOUR UNDERSTANDING

1. List the titles of professional health workers who treat mental disorders and emotional problems.
2. What are the two basic parts of psychotherapy?
3. What are two prescription drugs that are used in drug therapy?
4. What purpose do the drugs serve in drug therapy?
5. What is the difference between normal and abnormal fears?
6. How do guilt feelings turn into emotional problems?
7. What are the main characteristics of depression?
8. List three behaviors that are clues that a person may be suicidal.
9. How can you help a person who has talked about suicide?

Summary of Chapter 11

Human behavior is complex. The brain and body work together to cause actions. Your body gives off signals of mental activity when you are involved in problem situations. Sweaty hands and an upset stomach are examples.

Heredity plays a part in determining your behavior. Chromosomes pass inherited traits from parents to children. Some behavior traits run in families. Environment also influences behavior. Heredity and environment work together to shape your personality.

The basic emotions are love, anger, and fear. Emotions are the driving force that makes human relationships what they are. A good relationship begins with feelings of self-esteem or self-worth. Doing well at something or helping someone builds self-esteem.

Defense mechanisms are used to avoid hard problems. Limited use of defense mechanisms is normal. Some of the more common defense mechanisms are rationalization, daydreaming, negative behavior, repression, regression, and denial.

Emotional problems and mental disorders require treatment and therapy. Some common disorders are fear and anxiety, phobias, guilt, and depression. Deep or long-lasting depression can often lead to talk of suicide. Most people who think about suicide do not really want to die. There are signs of suicidal behavior to be aware of. There are certain things to do and not to do in dealing with a person who is thinking of committing suicide.

Psychiatrists, psychologists, counselors, and social workers are all professional mental health workers. Psychotherapy involves clarifying problems through gaining understanding. Psychotherapy is a useful treatment for a wide range of mental disorders. Group therapy, family therapy, and drug therapy are some ways to apply psychotherapy in treating emotional problems and mental disorders.

WORDS TO USE

1. *human behavior*
2. *biological*
3. *heredity*
4. *chromosome*
5. *environment*
6. *emotions*
7. *emotional health*
8. *love*
9. *self-esteem*
10. *self-worth*
11. *defense mechanisms*
12. *conflict*
13. *defensive*
14. *rationalization*
15. *daydreaming*
16. *negative behavior*
17. *repression*
18. *regression*
19. *denial*
20. *phobias*
21. *guilt*
22. *depression*
23. *suicide*
24. *psychotherapy*
25. *group therapy*
26. *family therapy*
27. *drug therapy*
28. *psychiatrist*

1. Why is it hard to learn about human behavior?
2. List some signals your body gives you when there is a problem in your mind.
3. Define the term *biological behavior.*
4. What does the old saying, "a chip off the old block," mean?
5. What are the basic emotions?
6. Describe the basis of emotional health.
7. What are some things that can build self-esteem?
8. Give the meaning of the term *defense mechanism.*
9. Give an example of the defense mechanism known as rationalization.
10. Why is daydreaming a defense mechanism?
11. What is regression?
12. How does denial work?
13. What is the meaning of the term phobia?
14. Describe depression.
15. List some of the signs people show when they might be thinking about suicide.
16. What happens during psychotherapy?
17. Describe group therapy.
18. What is involved in drug therapy?

To examine ways you can reduce injuries to yourself and others.

To identify methods of dealing with health emergencies.

KEY IDEAS:

Your own care and actions can prevent accidents.

Using proper first aid procedures can reduce injuries from accidents and other emergencies.

CHAPTER 12

Safety for Wellness

KEY IDEA #1:
Your own care and actions can prevent accidents.

It's Up to You

You can't avoid all accidents. Things happen that you cannot control. If a glass panel falls from the side of a tall building, pieces might hit you on the head. You may be severely hurt. You might even die.

This type of accident is very rare. Accidents that you can prevent happen all the time. If you use an unstable ladder to climb, or drive when you have been drinking, any accident that happens will be your fault. You cannot prevent the pieces of glass from hitting you. But you can avoid most accidents with cars and ladders.

These charts show the types of accidents that happen most frequently to young people in two age-groups.

5 - 14 Years Old	15 - 24 Years Old
Motor vehicle accidents	Motor vehicle accidents
Drowning	Drowning
Fire and burns	Firearms
Firearms	Poison
Falls	Fire and burns

Preventing Automobile Accidents

These rules can help prevent automobile accidents.

1. Use common sense.
2. Do not take chances.
3. Do not mix driving with alcohol or drugs.
4. Keep your vehicle in good working order.
5. Use recommended safety equipment.

These rules seem simple enough. Obviously, many people do not follow them. Otherwise, there would not be so many accidents.

Using **common sense** is the most important of all. All the other rules listed are based on this principle.

If you use common sense, you will not take chances. You will not drink or use drugs when you drive. You will never do anything else that might harm you or another person. Using common sense is a good habit to practice.

Using common sense means other things, too. Common sense means not driving when you are tired, or when road conditions are very bad. It means knowing your own weaknesses. If you have difficulty driving on a certain road at night, common sense tells you not to. If there are two roads that you can use to get to work, common sense tells you to take the safer route, even if it takes you longer. As the old saying goes, "It is better to be safe than sorry."

Do not take chances. When you drive, you must make decisions constantly. Should I pass this truck, even though I cannot see the road coming up? Should I try to make up for being late by driving over the speed limit? In these cases, you have to decide whether your actions will be dangerous or not. Nine times out of ten, passing the truck will not lead to an accident. But, what if this is the tenth time? If an accident happens, your whole life may be changed. Then you would wish that you could go back in time and make a different decision. Not taking chances might mean the difference between a normal life, and a life of mental and physical pain.

Do not drink or use drugs when you drive. Alcohol and drugs cause changes in your body. They affect your coordination. You cannot move as well as you usually do. They affect your judgment. This might cause you to take chances and drive recklessly. Most important, drugs and alcohol slow down reaction time. If an emergency arises, you take longer to react than you normally would.

You should always keep your vehicle in good working order. Faulty brakes or bald tires contribute to accidents. Additionally, you should use proper safety equipment. Always wear a seat belt. Statistics show that safety belts save lives. They also minimize injuries from accidents. When you travel with a small child, make sure the child is properly secured in a child safety seat or at least wearing a safety belt. Some states have laws requiring both adults and children to use this kind of safety equipment.

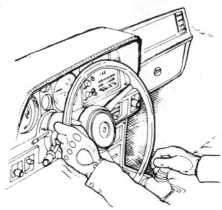

Using Other Vehicles

The same five safety rules also apply to bicycles, motorcycles, and other vehicles, only more so. When you are riding one of these smaller vehicles, you have to be even more cautious. These vehicles do not have roofs or sides to protect you in an accident.

When you ride one of these vehicles, stay away from other vehicles. Some automobile drivers get nervous when they are near a motorcycle or bicycle. They may drive strangely. Always wear an approved safety helmet. In a fall, the helmet will protect your head from serious damage.

Bicycle riders should think about how small and unprotected they are, in comparison with a car or truck. The law says bikers have the right of way. But insisting on this right can cause injuries and even death. It is foolish to ride a bicycle in heavy traffic. The chances for injury are much greater. Riders should also use hand signals when they want to turn or stop, just as a car driver does. Riders should also stay to the right and obey traffic signs. After all, bicycles are vehicles, just the same as cars. In order to use the roads together, all vehicles must follow the same rules.

Bicycle riders must also be aware of the road surface. Roads with bumps, potholes, or loose gravel are dangerous for bicycles.

Dealing With Fire

Fire is one of the leading causes of death and injury in the home. Most fires are caused by five things:

1. Improper disposal of cigarettes
2. Faulty electrical wiring
3. Improper storage of gasoline and other flammable substances
4. Overheated cooking oil
5. Children playing with matches

We can prevent fires by working to eliminate these causes.

First, make sure all cigarettes are out before you go to sleep. Some safety experts recommend that you never smoke in bed to avoid this problem. Better still, don't smoke at all. If you live in an older home, you should have a professional electrician check the wiring. Gasoline and other flammable substances should be placed in sealed metal containers. Experts recommend that these substances should be kept outside, away from your house. If cooking oil catches on fire, you can put out the fire by covering it with a metal cover or dousing it with sand, flour, or baking soda. Never try to put out a grease fire with water. The water will just spread the flames. You should keep matches and other lighters in a place where children cannot get them.

We cannot prevent all fires. That is why it is important to have **smoke detectors** in our homes. Smoke alarms tell you that there is a fire, even if you are asleep. They sound a loud alarm that will wake you. Generally, you will have enough time to get away from your house before the fire becomes too intense. Smoke detectors save lives. This is why many towns and cities have laws requiring their use. Smoke detectors should be installed on each level of your house.

If a fire breaks out in your house, do not panic. Get out of the building at once. You and your family should

have an escape plan. Be sure this plan has two ways for everyone in the house to escape. It is a good idea to have a rope ladder in every room that is above ground level. Feel all doors before you go through them. If they feel hot, use another escape route.

If your clothes catch on fire, you should stop, drop to the ground, and roll over to put out the fire. Safety experts call this "STOP, DROP, AND ROLL." It is an important rule to remember. If someone else's clothes have caught on fire, force the person down. Cover with a blanket or rug to put out the flames.

Install Smoke Detectors

Practice Escaping

Plan Your Escape

Test Door for Fire

Crawl Low in Smoke

Stop, Drop, and Roll to Put Out Flames

Preventing Other Accidents

You probably think that your home is a safe place. This is not true. More accidents happen in the home than any other place, with the exception of motor vehicles. Many people injure themselves by falling. To prevent falls, ask yourself these questions: Are toys and small objects put away? Are small rugs tacked down firmly? Are all areas well lit? Do you use a sturdy ladder instead of a wobbly chair? If you can answer "yes" to all of these, you have done your best to prevent falls. If not, you need to make some changes around your house.

Guns, knives, and other sharp objects should be kept where children cannot get them. Medicines, cleaning products, and other harmful materials should be put on a high shelf or in a locked cabinet. Children are curious about the things around them. At the same time, they don't have enough experience to know what is safe and what is harmful. Teens and adults have to protect children until the young ones are old enough to care for themselves.

Water Safety

Many injuries and deaths are the result of swimming accidents. Most of these accidents are preventable. You can keep yourself and others safe if you follow these rules:

1. Never go swimming alone. Use the buddy system. Check on your partner to see if he is in danger.

2. Swim only in protected areas where there is a lifeguard. Follow the lifeguard's directions.

3. Know your limitations. Don't try to push beyond them.

4. Pay attention to the weather. Get out of the water if it looks as if it is going to storm.

5. Don't dive into unfamiliar water. Check to see how deep the water is before you dive in.

Being careful and using common sense will prevent many accidents in the water.

CHECK YOUR UNDERSTANDING

1. List three ways to prevent automobile accidents.

2. Explain what using your common sense means.

3. Why can a bicycle be more dangerous than a car?

4. List three ways to prevent fires.

5. What should you do if your clothes catch on fire?

6. How can you prevent young children from being poisoned?

You Can Help

Have you ever read a story about a lifeguard who saves someone from drowning? The lifeguard jumps into the water. He pulls out the victim. He gives the victim mouth-to-mouth resuscitation. Meanwhile, a crowd gathers. They watch the guard and the victim anxiously. Finally, the victim begins to revive. The lifeguard has saved a life. Everyone admires the lifeguard.

While you were reading the story, didn't you wish that you were the lifeguard, saving someone's life? You can be that hero. With a working knowledge of first aid, you will know what to do to help people in an emergency.

First Aid

First aid is the immediate and temporary care given to a person with an injury or sudden illness. Immediate means that the care is given right away. Temporary means that the care is given until a trained medical helper takes over as a care giver. First aid has saved many lives.

What to Do First

In an emergency, the first thing you should do is call for professional help. Send someone else to get this aid. Never leave the victim alone. If there is a telephone nearby, ask the person to call the local emergency number. In most areas, this number is 911.

This number will put you in touch with the police, the fire department, and rescue squads that work in your area.

Keep calm. This will reassure the victim. It will also help you get to work immediately.

See that the victim is warm and comfortable. If the weather is cold, cover the victim with a coat or blanket. Look for a tag the victim may be wearing. This has special medical information needed to treat the victim.

Before you begin working, check the victim. See if he is breathing. Feel for a pulse. Look for any bleeding.

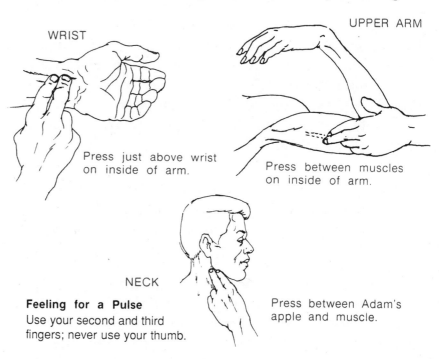

WRIST

Press just above wrist on inside of arm.

UPPER ARM

Press between muscles on inside of arm.

NECK

Feeling for a Pulse
Use your second and third fingers; never use your thumb.

Press between Adam's apple and muscle.

Never move an accident victim unless you have to. You might make his injuries even worse. If the victim is in danger, carefully move him away from the dangerous place.

Breathing Emergencies

Many accidents and injuries can cause a victim to stop breathing. Some of these are heart attacks, choking, drowning, electric shock, drug overdoses, and poisoning. No one can live without oxygen for more than a few minutes. If a victim has stopped breathing, you have to breathe for him. This is called **artificial respiration**. This technique forces air into the victim's lungs. The air gives his body the oxygen it needs.

Do not give artificial respiration until you know that someone has stopped breathing. Ask the victim a question, such as "Are you all right?" If he can answer, he is still breathing. Look at the chest, to see if it is moving. Put your ear near the victim's mouth and nose. You should be able to feel and hear breathing this way.

If you cannot find any signs of breathing, you must start artificial respiration right away. Try to clear an airway. This is the path air takes from the nose to the lungs. It is easy to do this. Put your hand under the victim's neck. Place your other hand on the victim's forehead. Push the forehead down and gently raise the neck. The victim's chin should be pointing upward. Use a finger to clear away any object that may be stuck in the victim's mouth.

Pinch the victim's nose. Take a deep breath and put your lips around his mouth. Blow four times. Raise your head and take another deep breath. Watch to see that the air you breathed in is coming back out. Continue giving breaths. Adults need a breath every five seconds. Children need a breath every three seconds. Continue artificial respiration until medical help arrives.

CPR

If you can't find a victim's pulse, his heart has stopped working. His cells aren't getting the oxygen they need. Something has to be done quickly. **Cardiopulmonary resuscitation** (CPR) is a technique that does the work of the heart and lungs until trained medical help arrives. The heart and lungs bring air into the body and transfer it to all body parts. The body uses blood to carry the oxygen.

You cannot learn CPR by reading a book. It requires special knowledge to know exactly what to do. But, you can learn about some of the things it involves, the ABCs of CPR. *A* stands for airway. The first part of CPR is making sure that the victim has a clear airway. This is also a part of artificial respiration. *B* stands for breathing. The second part of CPR is actually artificial respiration. *C* stands for chest compressions. This special technique involves pushing on a person's chest at exactly the right place, with exactly the right amount of pressure. You have to learn this technique in special classes. Chest compressions move blood through some parts of the body.

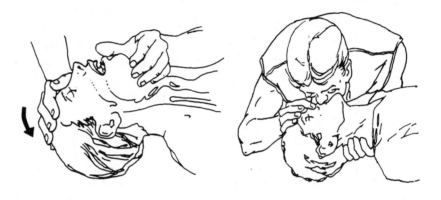

Open an airway.   Breathe for the victim.

Artificial Respiration

Choking

Choking victims need immediate attention. Their airway is blocked. Their bodies are not getting the oxygen they need. You can use the **Heimlich maneuver** to dislodge food or objects from the **trachea**. The trachea is the tubelike airway that stretches from the back of your mouth to your lungs. To do the Heimlich maneuver, stand behind the victim. Wrap your arms around him. Make a fist with one hand. Use your other hand to squeeze sharply at a point right below the victim's breastbone. Keep up the short bursts of squeezing until the object is forced out of the trachea.

The Heimlich Maneuver

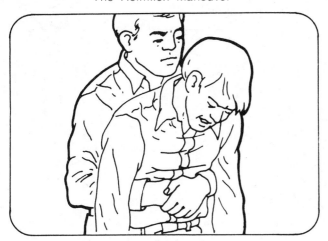

Controlling Bleeding

If you lose a large amount of blood, you can die. Serious bleeding must be controlled immediately to save a person's life. Someone providing first aid can use several techniques to do this.

One method is to apply direct pressure on the wound. Put a clean cloth over the wound. Press on the cloth with the palm of your hand. If you don't have a clean cloth, you can use your hand alone.

Do not remove the cloth or your hand. The blood will begin to **clot** soon. The body closes up the wound. Removing the cloth or your hand will start the bleeding again.

You can use two other methods to control bleeding. They are indirect methods. Do not attempt to use them unless you have more instruction on them.

The first technique is applying pressure to a body **pressure point**. These are places in the body where a

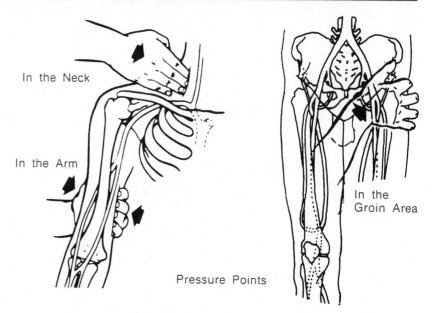

In the Neck

In the Arm

In the Groin Area

Pressure Points

large artery lies along a bone. If you press the artery against the bone, you can stop the flow of blood. If you want to stop bleeding from a wound in the arm, press on the artery under the arm. If you want to stop the bleeding from a wound in the leg, apply pressure to an artery in the groin area. Another indirect method you can use to stop bleeding is a **tourniquet**. A tourniquet is a tight band that stops the flow of blood to an area of the body. Use a tourniquet only if you have had the training to do so, and if you cannot stop the bleeding in any other way. If you do apply a tourniquet, do not remove it.

A Tourniquet

Treating Cuts

Wounds that bleed a lot usually do not become infected. The blood itself washes away the bacteria. Puncture wounds, scrapes, and other kinds of cuts do not bleed as much. These kinds of wounds need to be washed well with soap and water to prevent infection.

Puncture wounds are especially dangerous. They are caused by nails and other sharp objects. They are very deep, but the surface cut is very small. This surface area may close over quickly. But the injured part inside the body does not. It becomes a breeding ground for bacteria. A disease called **tetanus** can result. A doctor can give the victim a tetanus shot to prevent this from happening.

Poisoning

If you suspect that someone has been poisoned, call the **Poison Control Center** (PCC) for your area immediately. Poison Control Centers have been set up around the country. Experts staff their telephones twenty-four hours a day. They will tell you what to do for the victim.

The PCC may tell you that it is necessary to make the person vomit. They will probably recommend that you give him **syrup of ipecac** to do this. Anyone can purchase ipecac at the drugstore. People with small children often keep ipecac in their homes. The PCC will tell you to make the victim vomit only if the person has swallowed a **noncorrosive poison**. These are poisons like hair dye, cosmetics, bug spray, detergents, alcohol, aspirin, and most pills.

The Poison Control Center will tell you not to make a person vomit if a **corrosive poison** has been swallowed.

These are poisons that burn the inside of the mouth and body. If a person who has swallowed one of these poisons vomits, the poison will come up again and cause more damage. The PCC will probably tell you to give these victims milk to dilute the poison. Some examples of this kind of poison are paint thinner, oven cleaner, gasoline, kerosene, cleaning fluids, and bleach.

If a person has poison on his skin or in his eyes, the Poison Control Center will tell you to wash away the poison as quickly as possible. Keep flooding the poisoned area with water until medical help arrives.

Shock

Shock is a condition that often happens when a person is severely injured. Shock is a complicated reaction the body uses to protect itself. People who are in shock have many different symptoms. Some of these are weakness, a fast pulse, and cold, wet skin. If you suspect a victim is in shock, try to keep him warm. Put a blanket or other cover both under and over him. If the victim's legs are not injured, raise his feet slightly. Do not give the victim anything to eat or drink.

Burns

Burns can be serious injuries. They destroy body tissue and cause the body to lose vital fluids.

Burns are classified according to the amount of damage that they do to the body. **First-degree burns** are the least serious burn. The skin gets red. It looks like a bad sunburn. There is usually no scarring from this type of burn.

A **second-degree burn** is a more serious injury. The skin is blistered. There may be some scarring from this kind of injury.

Both first- and second-degree burns can be painful. The pain occurs because the nerves in the skin are destroyed. Cold water can ease the pain. You can put the burned area in cold water, or apply cold, wet cloths to the area. Do not use butter, lard, or oil on the burn. They can cause infections. If the skin has blisters, be careful not to break them. Cut clothing away from the victim's body instead of pulling it. Put a clean cloth over the burned area to keep out bacteria.

Third-degree burns are the most serious kind of burn. They injure many layers of body tissue. The victim may feel either intense pain or none at all. It can take months for this kind of burn to heal. Third-degree burns often cause scarring. Plastic surgery may be necessary to restore the burned area. Do not put water on this kind of burn. Treat the victim for shock. Get medical help immediately.

First-degree burns redden the skin.

Second-degree burns cause blisters.

Third-degree burns destroy many layers of tissue.

1. What is first aid?
2. What three things should you first check before trying to help a victim?
3. What is the difference between artificial respiration and CPR?
4. What is the Heimlich maneuver?
5. List three ways to control bleeding.
6. Why are puncture wounds so dangerous?
7. If you suspect a person has been poisoned, what should you do first?
8. How can you treat shock?
9. Describe a first-degree burn.

Summary of Chapter 12

You can prevent automobile accidents by following these rules: use common sense, do not take chances, do not drive when you have been using alcohol or drugs, keep your vehicle in good working order, and use recommended safety equipment. Be even more careful when riding a bicycle or motorcycle. They cannot protect you as a car does.

Fires can be prevented by being careful with matches and flammable substances and by supervising children carefully. Be sure that your home has smoke detectors on every level. Have a family escape plan to use in case of fire. If your clothes catch on fire, stop, drop, and roll.

Prevent accidents in the home by putting toys away, tacking down small rugs, keeping areas well lit, and using sturdy ladders. Keep medicines, cleaning products, and dangerous instruments away from small children. Be cautious around a pool or other body of water. Never dive into unfamiliar water.

Once an accident occurs, first aid can help a victim until professional medical workers arrive. If breathing has stopped, use artificial respiration. The Heimlich maneuver can help a choking victim. You can control serious bleeding by applying direct pressure, using pressure points, or applying a tourniquet. Wash other wounds with soap and water. A victim with a puncture wound should have a tetanus shot.

Depend on the advice of the local Poison Control Center to treat poison victims. The three types of burns require different kinds of treatment. Use cool water on first- and second-degree burns. Get immediate medical attention for third-degree burns.

WORDS TO USE

1. *common sense*
2. *first aid*
3. *artificial respiration*
4. *cardiopulmonary resuscitation (CPR)*
5. *Heimlich maneuver*
6. *clot*
7. *pressure point*
8. *tourniquet*
9. *puncture wounds*
10. *tetanus*
11. *Poison Control Center (PCC)*
12. *syrup of ipecac*
13. *noncorrosive poison*
14. *corrosive poison*
15. *shock*
16. *first-degree burns*
17. *second-degree burns*
18. *third-degree burns*
19. *smoke detectors*
20. *trachea*

REVIEW QUESTIONS FOR CHAPTER 12

1. List two ways of preventing automobile accidents.

2. What does this saying mean: "It is better to be safe than sorry"?

3. Why is it dangerous to use drugs or drink when you drive?

4. What should you do to keep safe on a bicycle?

5. How can you safely put out a grease fire?

6. How can smoke detectors save lives?

7. List five ways of making your home safe from accidents.

8. What does the term *first aid* mean?

9. What is the emergency number that you can use to contact the police, fire department, and rescue workers in your area?

10. Describe how artificial respiration helps a victim.

11. What are pressure points?

12. Why is vomiting not advised for a person who has swallowed a corrosive poison?

13. What are some of the symptoms of shock?

14. Which is the most serious kind of burn?

CHAPTER GOALS:

To understand that the family is a basic unit of society.

To see the relationship between individual health and family membership.

KEY IDEAS:

The family is a special group of people who are close and intimately acquainted.

Dating, courtship, and marriage are matters of interest and concern to families.

Family relationships involve decision-making about raising children and a wide variety of life situations.

CHAPTER 13

The Family

KEY IDEA #1:
The family is a special group of people who are close
and intimately acquainted.

Families

In your lifetime you usually have contact with two
families. The first family is the one into which you were
born. In this family you were a child and were taken care
of by your parents and others.

The second family will be your own. You will date, go
through a period of courtship, learn about the give and
take important to a healthy relationship, and then marry.
Marriage is the beginning of your second family. In your
marriage you think about having and raising children of
your own. Most people begin a family cycle with marriage,
followed by children who grow up to be young adults.
Then the cycle is ready to repeat itself. The young adults
take jobs, get married, and begin families of their own.

The Family Group

A mother and father and other children make up a **family**. The family is the basic unit of society. Members of a family are closely acquainted. They are at ease with each other and talk freely. Family members are very informal with each other. They share good times and bad times. Much of what happens in family circles is confidential. The family protects its members.

Family life is a special place for children. An atmosphere of support, love, affection, and caring provides a way toward a healthy life. In a family setting a child learns to communicate and to behave in acceptable ways. Sharing feelings and ideas leads to a belief system and a set of attitudes that work. Children prepare to face the outside world through their protected family experiences.

Adults, too, depend on family happenings and events as a major source of support. Concerns about work, school, social life, recreation, and health are all family matters. These are usually kept within the family circle.

Interest in families and family life has always been high. Many customs and laws in America are based on situations that center on individuals in a family setting. Responsibility for the education and rearing of their children falls to parents. All families are different, and as said earlier, much of what goes on within a family unit is confidential. However, laws have been established to define the kind of treatment that falls in the category of abuse. Child abuse laws are clear in their intent to provide protection for children, inside or outside their homes.

Family Needs and Expectations

Members of families react to each other on a special level, or "wavelength." Brothers and sisters have the knack for getting into family squabbles. Have you ever stopped to figure out why this might be? Most often it centers around who is getting the most attention. Naturally, when it is one person's turn to be in the limelight, the other person feels most "left out" or neglected. This natural conflict is called

sibling rivalry. One child or the other is always feeling left out or put upon. Teasing takes place. Children of varying ages within the family have different needs. Younger children do not always understand this. Each member of the family feels a need for attention. Often their actions are signals to other family members about these needs.

Adolescents find that family and school have increasing expectations of them. During a time when many physical and emotional changes are taking place, adolescents feel the added pressure of household chores and school workload. Teenagers try new activities at school. They try out new friendships. They spend more time away from the family. The family setting is both the cause of conflict and the place where conflicts can be worked out.

CHECK YOUR UNDERSTANDING

1. Briefly describe the two families that most of us experience.
2. What makes up the basic unit known as family?
3. Discuss the special part the family plays in the life of children.
4. What is meant by sibling rivalry?
5. List some special events for adolescents that may change the way they deal with their family.

Dating, Courtship, and Marriage

Members of the opposite sex begin to feel some
attraction for each other in adolescence. These normal
feelings are beginning signs of physical maturity. Social
customs and these newfound feelings lead to **dating**. A
date is a social event between a boy and a girl. They may
go to a game, to a movie, to a party, or to some other kind
of event where couples gather. A first date for a teen is
a big event in her or his life. It is also important for the
family of the teen.

Dating is a learning experience. You learn about your
own feelings and attitudes. You learn how to make
conversation and how to deal socially with the opposite
sex. As a result of dating, you develop a picture of the
kind of person you may want to spend more of your time
with. You learn that in addition to a certain normal
physical attraction, you enjoy the company of people
who have interests like yours. You may share an interest
in sports, music, movies, art, or reading. The common
ground sparks a relationship that may lead to serious
dating.

Going Steady

When a couple begins to share all of their dating time,
they are **going steady**. Going steady may last anywhere
from a day to a month, a year, or even several years.
Going steady may be fun. However, it may get into a
pattern of higher and higher expectations where more
and more problems enter the picture. Problems may
lead to "breaking up." While this is a difficult time for
most young people, it is a time to learn how to face real-
life problems.

Courtship

Courtship is an attempt to gain the affections of a partner. Courtship is seen as a more formal kind of dating, with marriage in mind. The social skills and the kinds of responsibilities involved in courtship take on very serious meaning. Feelings of romance and love are a part of thinking about and choosing a marriage partner.

Engagement

A further step in the process of man-woman relationships is the **engagement** to be married. Not everyone gets engaged, but those who do make a formal commitment to each other. Plans for marriage are talked over. Subjects related to all phases of living together and sharing responsibilities are discussed. The engaged couple finds out ways in which they are suited for one another. Basic values and life goals are brought out into the open. The couple learns to work together to solve problems. Important matters involve children, finances, male and female family roles, and education. Who you marry is important. Communicating about that marriage and what it might hold for each partner is also important.

Marriage

Marriage is a mutual or shared relationship between a husband and wife. Marriage is a legal matter, and it requires a marriage license from the state. Property, financial responsibilities, and care of children become a part of the marriage. Married couples usually set up their own households. The families they create are the basic social units for dealing with the schools, church, and social agencies. Communities are a mixture of families in a certain area.

Marriage is an emotional matter as well. Most people think of their family as the most important part of their life. Marriage is an arrangement where consideration, respect, love, and caring form the basis of operation. Shared experiences bring pleasure. The partners grow in trust of each other. Experience and understanding help to strengthen a marriage.

Teenage Marriage

People's behavior changes as they mature. Early relationships between people do not have the benefit of that maturity. Teenagers are weighed down with a growing list of individual responsibilities. Their bodies are changing. They are experiencing emotional extremes of ups and downs. Their education is still in progress. They have yet to gain job experience and financial independence. However, a number of teenagers get married. The odds of their success are limited.

Why People Get Married

Marriage is a highly personal matter. Marriage involves love and **commitment**. Commitment means working toward making something happen. A successful marriage is measured by the partners themselves. How strongly they work toward daily and long-term goals is one measure. The achievements of a working marriage add strength to the initial bond of love and caring that started the marriage. Commitment and good communication between partners are key factors.

In some cases, marriage is entered into for wrong reasons. Some marriages are based upon pressures brought by family or friends. Some people blindly follow their friends into marriage. Some young people want to escape from homes where they are unhappy. Sometimes early pregnancies bring pressure to marry. Some early marriages seem to work out just fine. Others fall to problems of money, immaturity, and lack of commitment.

CHECK YOUR UNDERSTANDING
1. What is dating all about?
2. Describe the difference between just dating and going steady.
3. What are some purposes of courtship?
4. What are some things that happen when there is an engagement between a couple?
5. What are three main features of marriage?
6. What are some things that are true about most teenage marriages?
7. List some reasons that people get married.

KEY IDEA #3:
Family relationships involve decision-making about
raising children and a wide variety of life situations.

Communication

Problems and situations always come up when people are doing things together. How people deal with them makes a difference in how their life together moves along. Expressing opinions and working out some kind of agreement are important to the success of a marriage. Part of the art of communicating is being a good listener. Not everyone is naturally good at listening to what someone else is saying. It takes practice to learn the art of being a good listener.

Running a Household

Cooperation and **communication** have always been at the center of running a **household**. Matters like handling the checkbook and helping children with their homework require talking and listening. Daily chores that husbands and wives are faced with take time, effort, and energy. These activities call for a **commitment** from both people.

Living together in a successful and harmonious way depends on some level of emotional maturity. Both partners need to make adjustments and cope with a wide variety of life situations. Matters involving money and financing of projects are both daily and long-term concerns. Talking about whether there is enough money for what is needed and what is wanted is a good idea.

Marriage can be a very satisfying and happy relationship. Often it is. This does not mean that there will not be difficulties and hard times. There will be. The most common problems come from lack of communication. These problems focus on money matters, taking one another for granted, and on changing values and goals over time. The best intentions of many people may go astray. Some couples find their marriage problems so difficult that they seek a separation and a divorce.

Divorce

Divorce is the legal dissolving of the marriage. Divorce is the last step for couples after they have tried to work things out to improve their marriage. Divorce involves dividing property, splitting up a household, and sharing in the responsibilities for any children. Each year in the United States about 2,000,000 marriages take place. Over one-half end in divorce. Why do so many marriages go this route?

Sometimes during the relationship one or both partners develop conflicts. The conflicts may be about values, handling of money, relations with in-laws, differences over children, or matters of sexuality. In some instances, people have simply mistakenly married the wrong person.

Sometimes one partner gets into the routine of blaming the other for everything that goes wrong—rightly or wrongly. In some cases one or both partners have grown up in families where divorce has been common. They are more likely to follow that pattern than those partners who have had no divorce in their family background. Marriages fail for a number of reasons. The basic failures center on things that interfere with commitment and with good communication between the partners.

Teenage marriages have a higher rate of failure than the general population. About two of every three teen marriages end in divorce. The cause for this high rate of failed marriages among teens is immaturity, along with financial problems.

Child Abuse and Child Neglect

Child abuse is a widespread problem. Children are sometimes physically abused and injured. They are mentally mistreated through verbal and emotional attacks. Child abuse is a serious matter that generally requires outside assistance. Most communities have established a hotline for children, parents, and other concerned persons to seek help. Parents who abuse their children are likely to have problems that require professional help.

Child neglect involves withholding basic needs such as health care, education, food and shelter, safety, and emotional care. Why do parents abuse or neglect their own children? There is no one reason. Lack of maturity, use of alcohol and other drugs, financial problems, early unwanted pregnancies, and general lack of knowledge about parenting are all given as reasons. Sometimes parents do not know the difference between discipline and abuse. Many times children get blamed for family shortcomings. Some parents believe that because the children are theirs, they can do anything they want to with them. In many cases, parents who practice child abuse and child neglect were victims of those same practices when they were children.

A serious form of child abuse is **sexual abuse**. Any kind of sexual involvement of adults with children is called sexual abuse. Children who are being sexually abused need to let someone know, and to get help.

CHECK YOUR UNDERSTANDING

1. What part does communication play in the success of a marriage?

2. What are some of the major events in running a household?

3. What behaviors are needed to run a household?

4. What is the meaning of divorce?

5. What are some possible causes for divorce?

6. What reasons are there for the high rate of divorce in teenage marriages?

7. What is involved in child abuse?

8. What is meant by child neglect?

Summary of Chapter 13

The family is the basic unit of society. Family life provides a special place for children to grow up. It provides protection and security. The family is also the center of life activities for most adults. Many customs and laws center on the role of family life and individual responsibilities within the family. Social, emotional, and educational events are the center of family life. Adolescence is a period when the family is both an anchor in a storm and a place to learn to handle responsibility.

Dating, going steady, courting, and being engaged are all matters of interest to and part of family life. Individuals learn how to know one another and to make decisions about how to get along. Communication skills are learned at all of the stages of going together.

Marriage is a legal event, a social event, and an emotional experience. Mature love forms the most favorable foundation for a successful marriage. Marriage can be very satisfying and enjoyable. The keys to a successful marriage are commitment and communication.

Teenage marriages do not have the benefit of maturity. They may lack financial strength and may end in divorce. Divorce is the legal ending of a marriage.

Child abuse and child neglect are major problems. Some parents physically and mentally mistreat their children. Increased public interest and awareness of child abuse have led to the establishment of child abuse hotlines in most communities.

WORDS TO USE

1. family
2. sibling rivalry
3. dating
4. going steady
5. courtship
6. engagement
7. marriage
8. commitment
9. communication
10. household
11. divorce
12. child neglect
13. child abuse
14. sexual abuse

REVIEW QUESTIONS FOR CHAPTER 13

1. How does the idea of "life cycles" fit the idea of families?

2. What are the two families that a person usually has contact with?

3. Describe family life as a special place for children.

4. What role does the family have for adults?

5. What is sibling rivalry?

6. What part do dating and going steady have to play in family life?

7. What is the purpose of courtship and engagement?

8. How should people think about their future and family in relation to themselves as individuals?

9. What are some of the ways to describe what marriage is?

10. What seems to be a problem with teenage marriages?

11. List some reasons that people get married.

12. What is meant by good communication skills?

13. What does divorce have to do with the law?

14. List some causes for divorce.

15. What is meant by the term *child abuse*?

16. What is involved in child neglect?

17. What is meant by the term sexual abuse?

18. If a person knows that a child is being abused, what can he or she do?

Appendix A: The Skeletal System

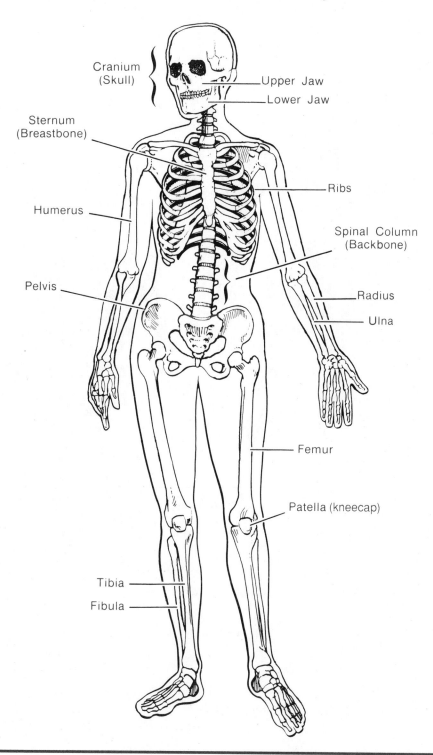

Cranium (Skull)

Upper Jaw

Lower Jaw

Sternum (Breastbone)

Ribs

Humerus

Spinal Column (Backbone)

Pelvis

Radius

Ulna

Femur

Patella (kneecap)

Tibia

Fibula

Appendix B: Your Muscles

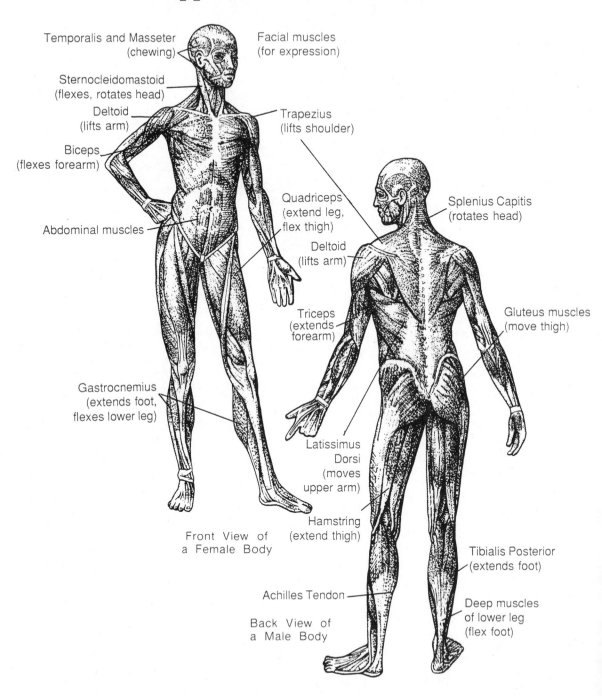

Temporalis and Masseter (chewing)

Facial muscles (for expression)

Sternocleidomastoid (flexes, rotates head)

Deltoid (lifts arm)

Biceps (flexes forearm)

Trapezius (lifts shoulder)

Abdominal muscles

Quadriceps (extend leg, flex thigh)

Deltoid (lifts arm)

Splenius Capitis (rotates head)

Gluteus muscles (move thigh)

Triceps (extends forearm)

Gastrocnemius (extends foot, flexes lower leg)

Latissimus Dorsi (moves upper arm)

Hamstring (extend thigh)

Front View of a Female Body

Tibialis Posterior (extends foot)

Achilles Tendon

Deep muscles of lower leg (flex foot)

Back View of a Male Body

Important Muscles of the Human Body

Appendix C: Digestive System

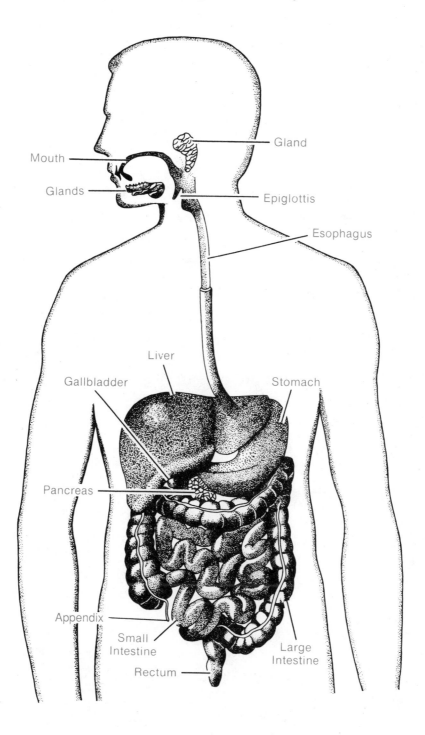

Mouth

Glands

Gland

Epiglottis

Esophagus

Liver

Gallbladder

Stomach

Pancreas

Appendix

Small
Intestine

Rectum

Large
Intestine

Glossary

acne — skin disorder causing pimples and blackheads

acquired immune deficiency syndrome (AIDS) — fatal infectious disease that destroys the immune defense system

adenoid — piece of tissue at the back of the mouth

adolescence — period of increased development in humans during puberty

adolescent — person at a life stage between childhood and adulthood

adolescent support team — group that helps an adolescent with problems

aerobic exercise — exercise that improves cardiovascular fitness

AIDS — acquired immune deficiency syndrome

alcohol — intoxicating drug produced by fermenting food substances

alcoholic — person who continues to drink until intoxicated

Alcoholics Anonymous (AA) — organization that treats alcoholics and their families

alcoholism — disease in which people cannot control their drinking

allergy — hives, breathing problem, or other response to particular substances in the environment

alveoli — microscopic air bags in the lungs

Alzheimer's disease — condition of the elderly that affects memory and other mental processes

amino acid — small chemical unit that makes up proteins

angina pectoris — chest pain due to lack of oxygen in the heart muscles

anorexia nervosa — disease in which people are obsessed with their weight and may starve to become thin

antibiotic — drug that fights germs

antibodies — proteins in plasma that fight disease

anus — opening in the rectum where solid wastes pass out

aorta — largest artery that takes oxygen-rich blood from the heart to the body

appendicitis — inflammation and swelling of the appendix, possibly leading to a burst appendix

arteriole — tiny artery carrying blood away from the heart

artery — blood vessel that carries oxygen and food to capillaries

arthritis — disease in which joints are inflamed and sore

artificial respiration — technique of forcing air into the lungs of a person who has stopped breathing

asthma — allergic reaction causing difficulty in breathing

atherosclerosis — clogging and narrowing of the arteries

athlete's foot — itching and cracking between the toes

auditory nerve — group of sensory neurons that send information from the ear to the brain

automatic activity — something the body does without thinking, such as digesting food or breathing

autonomic nervous system — the part of the nervous system that regulates the body's automatic responses

backbone — set of bones called vertebrae

bacteria — microorganisms that are both helpful and harmful to humans

ball-and-socket-joint — shoulder or hip joint

barbiturate — sleep-inducing drug

basal metabolic rate — speed at which energy from food is used by the body

basic life function — activity that all living things carry out: getting food; moving body; growing; sensing and reacting; using food and removing wastes; developing; and reproducing

benign — noncancerous

bicep — muscle in the upper arm

bile — chemical that breaks apart fat molecules; produced in liver, stored in gallbladder

biological activity — actions of the body

blood — special fluid that transports materials to keep the body healthy

blood alcohol level (BAL) — amount of alcohol in the blood

blood pressure — measure of how hard blood is pushing against artery walls

blood vessel — artery, vein, or capillary

body system — responsible for basic life functions of body; humans have nine systems that work together to keep the body working and healthy

body tissues — groups of similar cells in the body

bone — body part made of hard, living material

braces — appliances used to straighten teeth

brain — control center of the body

brain stem — connects the brain and spinal cord

bronchi — tubes that connect the trachea and lungs

bronchiole — small tube in the lung

bruise — black and blue mark caused by injury to a muscle

bulimia — disease in which people gorge and make themselves throw up

bypass surgery — surgery to correct a blocked artery

caffeine — stimulant found in coffee, soft drinks, and chocolate

calcium — mineral needed for bone formation; found in milk, dairy products, and leafy vegetables

calorie — unit for measuring heat; different foods have different caloric values

cancer — disease in which cell growth is abnormal and uncontrolled

capillary — smallest blood vessels in body; thin walls allow nutrients and oxygen to pass from bloodstream to cells

carbohydrate — "fuel chemical" that supplies the body with energy

carbon monoxide — harmful gas released when tobacco is burned

carcinogen — cancer-causing substance

cardiac muscle — involuntary muscle found in the heart

cardiopulmonary resuscitation (CPR) — technique of compressing chest and forcing air into the lungs of a person whose heart has stopped beating

cardiovascular disease — disorder of the heart or blood vessels

cardiovascular fitness — ability of the circulatory system to get oxygen to the cells

cardiovascular system — body system that includes the heart and blood vessels

cartilage — strong tissue that is not as hard as bone; the nose and knee contain cartilage

cataract — clouding of the lens of the eye

cavity — hole in a tooth caused by decay

cell — basic unit of life

cellulose — indigestible, hard part of plants; provides body with fiber, or bulk

central nervous system — made up of the brain and spinal cord, which send and receive messages; coordinates all activity of entire nervous system

cerebellum — brain part that controls balance and coordinates muscular activity

cerebral palsy — disease that affects the muscles

cerebrum — brain part that controls thinking, feelings, and body movement

characteristic — quality or trait

chemotherapy — treatment of cancer with massive doses of chemicals

child abuse — physical and mental mistreatment of children

child neglect — withholding basic needs from children

chlamydia — sexually transmitted disease that causes itching and burning of the genitals

cholesterol — found in animal fats; high levels may lead to heart disease

chromosome — tiny body in a cell's nucleus that carries genetic information

chronic bronchitis — long-lasting cough and inflammation of the bronchiole tubes

chronic disease — disorder that continues over a long period of time

circulatory system — body system made up of the heart, blood vessels, and blood; transports blood through the body

cirrhosis — liver disease caused by alcoholism

clot — gel or thicken

cocaine — highly addictive stimulant, especially in the form of crack

commitment — working toward making something happen

common sense — good judgment

communicable disease — illness passed from one organism to another; infectious disease

communication — process of talking and listening

conflict — disagreement or difference

connective tissue — special cells that hold the other tissue together

constipation — pain or difficulty when moving the bowels

convulsion — seizure or fit

cope — handle a situation in a calm manner

cornea — clear, transparent eye covering

corneal transplant — replacement of a damaged cornea with a fresh cornea from a donor

coronary artery — branch of the aorta that brings blood to the heart itself

coronary disease — heart disease

corpus luteum — follicle gland in the ovary that manufactures the hormone progesterone

corrosive poison — poison that burns the inside of mouth and body (examples are gasoline, kerosene, cleaning fluids)

courtship — participating in social activities that lead to engagement and marriage

cranium — skull, that part which encloses the brain

cystitis — infection of the bladder that causes pain during urination

dandruff — flaking of the scalp

dating — socializing between boys and girls on a one-to-one basis

daydreaming — placing oneself in a make-believe world

decision making — making choices

defense mechanism — behavior used to avoid facing problems

denial — denying reality by pretending there is no problem and thus avoiding a solution to the problem

depressant — substance that slows body activity

depression — long-lasting condition of sadness and dejection

dermatologist — skin doctor

dermis — inner layer of the skin

detached retina — loosening of the retina from the rest of the eye

diabetes — disease in which the body cannot make insulin, causing too much sugar in the blood

diaphragm — strong muscle under the lungs that helps in breathing

diarrhea — watery bowel movements

diastolic pressure — blood pressure reading when the heart muscle relaxes; the lower of the two readings

digestion — breaking down food to a form that cells can use

digestive system — stomach, small intestine, and other organs responsible for breaking down food

divorce — legal dissolving of a marriage

drug — nonfood substance that changes the mind or body

drug addiction — dependency on a drug

drug hotline — free telephone number that can be used to get help for a drug problem

drug therapy — use of medicine to treat mental or emotional disorders

eardrum — thin tissue separating the outer and inner ear

egg or egg cell — female cell involved in reproduction

embryo — first stage in early growth of a human being

emotions — feelings

emotional health — an aspect of wellness; one measure of emotional health centers on how individuals deal with the emotional ups and downs of life

emotional well-being — having a positive attitude and a good self-concept

emphysema — serious respiratory disorder causing difficulty in breathing

enamel — nonliving, outer layer of the teeth

engagement — time period when a couple has made a commitment to marry

environment — surroundings

enzyme — chemical in an organism that does a special job such as digesting food

epidermis — outer layer of the skin

epiglottis — small flap of tissue that prevents food from getting into the trachea

epilepsy — disease marked by convulsive seizures

erection — hardening and enlarging of the penis

esophagus — tube connecting the mouth and stomach

essential amino acid — chemical the body cannot make and must get by eating protein

estrogen — hormone that causes changes in the female such as breast development

excretion — getting rid of waste materials

excretory system — body system that gets rid of wastes

exhaling — breathing out

experience — previous behavior

eye donor — person who donates his or her eyes to medical science after death

fallopian tube — duct where the egg is fertilized

family — group of people who are close and intimately acquainted

family therapy — group therapy involving several family members

farsightedness — difficulty in seeing up close

fat — nutrient that provides the body with energy

feces — solid waste material in the large intestine

femur — thigh bone; longest bone in body

fertilization — union of the egg and the sperm

fetal alcohol syndrome — physical and mental disorders in babies born to alcoholic mothers

fetus — human being developing in uterus

fibula — lower leg bone

first aid — immediate and temporary care given to a person with an injury or illness

first-degree burn — burn producing red skin like a sunburn

flexibility — ability to twist, turn, stretch, and bend easily

flossing — using dental floss to clean between the teeth

fluoride — chemical that prevents cavities

follicle — structure inside the ovaries where eggs develop

fracture — break in a bone

fraternal twin — twin formed when two eggs are fertilized at the same time

function — job

fungus — organism growing in damp places

gallbladder — pouch attached to liver that stores and releases bile to aid digestion

gallstone — small, hard mass in the gallbladder causing pain

gangly — long, thin, and awkward

gastric juice — chemical secreted by stomach walls that breaks down food

gene — the part of a chromosome that contains DNA

genetics — study of heredity

genetic makeup — genes in an organism

genital — relating to the pubic area

genital herpes — sexually transmitted disease that causes blisters in the genitals

German measles — disease causing defects in unborn babies

germ theory — concept that germs cause disease

gestation — the period of pregnancy

gland — structure that makes a substance to help the body work

glaucoma — incresed pressure in the eyeball

gliding joint — connects the vertebrae and allows back to move easily

glucose — form of sugar used by the body to provide energy

going steady — when two people date only each other

gonorrhea — sexually transmitted disease that can cause sterility

good health — wellness; a person's physical, emotional, and social well-being

group therapy — talk sessions among people with similar psychological problems

guilt — feeling responsible for causing a problem

hallucination — strange vision

hangover — nausea, vomiting, and other symptoms as a result of drinking too much alcohol

hay fever — allergy to certain grasses

head lice — insects that infest the scalp

health — wellness; physical, mental, and social well-being

hearing aid — device that helps some hearing impaired people

heart — powerful pump that forces blood through the body

heart attack — heart stoppage due to insufficient blood supply

heart murmur — slight malfunction of the heart valves

heart rate — speed at which the heart beats

Heimlich maneuver — procedure for dislodging food from the trachea of a choking victim

hemoglobin — substance in red blood cells that attracts oxygen

heredity — passing of traits from parents to children

heroin — extremely habit-forming street drug

hinge joint — knee joint

hive — red, raised area of the skin; allergic reaction to substance

hormone — chemical messenger that helps regulate body functions

HTLV-III — retrovirus that causes AIDS

human behavior — how humans act

humerus — upper arm bone

hypertension — high blood pressure

identical twin — twin formed from a single egg

immune system — body system that fights infection

immunity — ability to resist disease

indigestion — gas or another problem related to digestion

infection — area invaded by a germ

infectious disease — disease passed from one organism to another

inferior vena cava — large vein through which blood enters the right atrium

influenza — viral infection; the flu

inhalant — something that is inhaled; for example, medicine for asthma or dangerous substances such as glue or paint thinner

inhaling — breathing in

inherited trait — quality passed from parent to child

insulin — hormone in the pancreas that regulates the amount of sugar in the blood

interferon — chemical messenger that tells cells what to do

intoxicated — drunk

involuntary muscle — muscle that works automatically

ipecac — syrup to induce vomiting

joint — place where bones meet

kidney failure — inability of the kidney to purify the blood

kidney transplant — putting the kidney of a donor into the body of a person with kidney failure

large intestine — organ that removes excess water from undigested food and forms solid wastes

larynx — voice box

lean body composition — ratio of fat to muscle in the body

left atrium — upper left heart chamber that gets oxygen-rich blood from the lungs

left ventricle — lower left heart chamber that sends oxygen-rich blood through the aorta and to the body

lens — eye part that changes shape to focus light

leukemia — cancer of the blood

life-style — behavior based upon what an individual finds important

ligament — special tissue connecting bones at a movable joint

liver — organ that makes bile, which is used in the process of digestion

love — basic human emotion focusing on the need for relationships; necessary for normal emotional health

LSD — drug that causes hallucinations

lung cancer — cancer usually caused by cigarette smoking

malignant — cancerous

malocclusion — improper bite

mammogram — breast x-ray

marijuana — common street drug with varying effects on different people

marriage — legal, shared relationship between husband and wife

marrow — substance in bones that makes blood cells

master gland — pituitary gland

maturity — adulthood

medulla — brain part that controls automatic body activities such as breathing and circulation

melanin — pigment that gives skin its color

meningitis — infectious disease of the spinal membrane that responds to antibiotic treatment; if untreated paralysis or death may result

menstruation — discharging of blood from the uterus through the vagina

mental activity — actions of the mind

mental health professional — psychiatrist, psychologist, counselor, or social worker

mental well-being — good emotional health

microbe — microscopic germ

microorganism — very tiny organism that can only be seen under the microscope

migraine headache — painful, long-lasting headache

mineral — nutrient necessary for living things

molar — back, grinding tooth

mole — dark bump on the skin

morphine — narcotic drug used as a painkiller

multiple sclerosis — nerve disease resulting in various forms of disability

muscle — body part responsible for movement

muscle tone — the constant state of partial contraction of certain muscles in the body; this tension holds up the body

muscular dystrophy — disease in which muscle fiber is gradually destroyed

muscular endurance — ability of muscles to work for a long period of time

muscular strength — amount of force muscles exert to overcome resistance

narcotic — drug that causes physical addiction

nearsightedness — difficulty in seeing from a distance

negative — pessimistic, downhearted, discouraged

negative behavior — saying no to everything

nephron — tiny tube in the kidney that filters blood

nerve — specialized cell that receives and transmits messages

nicotine — stimulant found in tobacco

noncommunicable disease — disease caused by a disorder within the body rather than pathogens; not spread from one person to another

noncorrosive poison — poison that does not burn the digestive system

nostrils — openings at the end of the nose

nutrients—the six chemicals—water, carbohydrates, fats, proteins, minerals, and vitamins—that organisms need to stay alive

nutrition — study of foods and how the body uses them

ophthalmologist — medical doctor specializing in eye care

optic nerve — group of sensory neurons that send information from the eye to the brain

optimistic — hopeful, confident

optometrist — licensed technician qualified to examine eyes and prescribe glasses

organ — a basic working part of an organism formed from different types of tissues acting together

organism — a living being

organized — arranged in a system

orthodontist — dentist specializing in straightening teeth

osteoporosis — disease in which bones become brittle and break easily

otosclerosis — middle ear disease resulting in hearing loss

ovarian cycle — 28-day cycle in which ovulation and menstruation occur

ovary — female gland that produces and encloses egg cells

---

over-the-counter drug—medicine that can be purchased without a prescription

ovulation — production of eggs by the ovaries, usually occurring monthly in humans

oxygenated — containing oxygen

pancreas — large digestive gland that produces insulin, which helps cells use sugar

Pap smear — procedure to detect cervical cancer

paralysis — loss of the ability to move

pathogen — germ, or disease-causing organism

PCP — drug that causes hallucinations and violent behavior

peer —- person of the same age and social group

peer counselor — person in the same age-group who helps with problems

peer pressure — pressure from friends or classmates that influences actions

pelvis — hip bone

penis — male organ of reproduction

periodontal disease — gum disease leading to loose teeth

peripheral nerve — nerve that sends messages between the central nervous system and other body parts

personality — what you are, what you do, and your reasons for doing things; a person's behavioral and emotional characteristics

perspiration — waste material that passes through the skin; sweat

philosophy of life — way of looking at the world

phobia — intense, irrational, unfounded fear

physical addiction — physical dependence upon a substance

physical fitness — having the energy to do what you want; muscular strength and endurance, flexibility, and cardiovascular fitness are all aspects

physical well-being — good physical health

pinkeye — contagious eye infection

pituitary gland — gland that sends out hormones to control the actions of other glands; master gland

pivot joint — rotating joint, such as the elbow and the place where the head meets the vertebrae

plaque — film on the teeth which can lead to tooth and gum disease

plasma — liquid part of blood

platelet — substance in plasma that helps clot blood

pneumonia — disease of the lungs

Poison Control Center — place to call for immediate, 24-hour information about treatment for poisoning

polyunsaturated fat — fat that does not raise the cholesterol level

pore — tiny opening in the skin

positive — cheerful, rosy, optimistic

pregnant — carrying a developing human being in the uterus

prescription drug — medicine ordered by a physician

pressure point — point on an artery that can be pressed to control bleeding

preventive medicine — steps taken to avoid rather than cure a disease

problem-solving — highest kind of learned behavior

progesterone — pre-pregnancy hormone that causes changes in the uterine wall

protein — chemical needed for growth and repair of body tissues and for body maintenance

psychiatrist — medical doctor specializing in mental and emotional problems

psychological addiction — emotional dependence upon a substance

psychotherapy — treatment for psychological problems and disorders

puberty — period in life in which children develop into adults and reach sexual maturity

pubic hair — hair in the genital area

pulmonary artery — tube that carries blood from the heart to the lungs

pulmonary vein — tube that carries blood from the lungs back to the heart

puncture wound — break in the skin caused by a sharp object

pupil — the part of the eye that gets larger and smaller when exposed to light

radiation therapy — treatment of cancer with radiation

radius — lower arm bone

rationalization — making up excuses that do not fit a situation

reaction time — amount of time it takes to respond to a situation

reasoning — making connections between ideas

receptor or receptor cell — cell in a sense organ that receives and transmits information

rectum — lower part of the large intestine

red blood cell — part of blood that carries oxygen

reflex — automatic reaction to a stimulus

regression — reacting to problems with childlike behavior

repression — hidden behaviors and feelings; escaping a problem by not remembering it

reproductive organ — ovary or testes

reproductive system — body system which differs in males and females and which produces babies

respiration — inhaling of oxygen and exhaling of carbon dioxide

respiratory system — system of tubes and organs enabling the body to bring in oxygen and get rid of carbon dioxide

retina — eye part that helps send information to the brain

retrovirus — strange-behaving virus

rheumatic fever — bacterial infection which may cause heart disease; may result from untreated strep throat

rib — bone that protects the heart and lungs

right atrium — upper right heart chamber that receives oxygen-poor blood from the body

right ventricle — lower right heart chamber that sends blood to the lungs for oxygen

ringworm — infection of the scalp and skin caused by fungus

saliva — liquid found in glands in the mouth; contains a chemical that breaks down food

sanitation — process of making things free of filth and infectious material

saturated fat — fat that raises the cholesterol level

sebum — oily substance secreted by oil glands that lubricates the body

secrete — give off, such as glands giving off chemicals

second-degree burn — burn producing blisters and some scarring

self-concept — your opinion of yourself

self-esteem — good feelings about yourself; confidence and satisfaction in yourself

self-image — how you see yourself

self-worth — good feeling about yourself that stems from recognition, trust, and self-confidence

semen — fluid from the penis that contains sperm

senility — condition that affects the mental processes of older people

sense organs — eyes, ears, nose, tongue, and skin; take in signals from the outside world

sense receptor — cell that picks up information about heat, cold, light, sound, and other outside stimuli and relays it to the brain

sex gland — ovary or testes

sexual abuse — sexual mistreatment of people, including children

sexual intercourse — insertion of the penis into the vagina

sexually mature — able to reproduce

sexually transmitted disease (STD) — disease transmitted by sexual contact

shock — weakness, rapid pulse, clammy skin, and other body reactions to severe injury

sibling rivalry — conflict between brothers and sisters

sickle-cell anemia — genetic disorder which affects red blood cells

signing, sign language — method of communication using hand movements

skeletal muscle — voluntary muscle that causes movement

skeletal system — network of bones that support the body and give it shape

small intestine — digestive organ in humans where most digestion takes place

social well-being — getting along with other people

sodium — essential mineral; table salt

sperm — male cell involved in reproduction

sphygmomanometer — device used to take blood pressure

spinal column — backbone or vertebrae

spinal cord — the major nerve cord running down the back of vertebrates

spleen — organ that destroys old red blood cells

STD — sexually transmitted disease

sterile — unable to reproduce

sternum — breastbone

stethoscope — device used to listen to the heart

stimulant — substance that increases activity of the central nervous system

stomach — digestive organ between the esophagus and small intestine

strabismus — eye muscle weakness

streptococcus — infection-causing bacterium

stress — set of physical and emotional reactions brought on by pressure

stress network — web formed by the interactions of individuals with the people they know

stroke — condition caused by lack of blood to the brain

sty — pimple on the eyelid

suicide — act of intentionally taking one's own life

superior vena cava — large vein through which blood enters the right atrium

sweat gland — coiled tube at the outside of the skin that lets out perspiration

syphilis — serious sexually transmitted disease caused by a bacterium; open sores are an early symptom

systolic pressure — blood pressure reading when heart muscle contracts; the higher of the two readings

tar — substance in cigarette smoke that causes lung cancer

tendon — tough tissue that attaches muscles to bones

tension — stress and strain in muscles or nerves

testes — gland in males that produces sperm cells

testosterone — hormone that causes changes in males such as the production of facial hair

tetanus — bacterial disease often contracted from a puncture wound

tetracycline — antibiotic

third-degree burn — very serious and painful burn injuring many layers of tissue and often causing permanent scars

throat culture — cultivating material from the throat for bacteria

tibia — shin bone

tissue — group of similar cells that act together to do certain jobs

tolerance — body's ability to get used to a drug

tonsil — tissue at the back of the mouth

tonsillitis — infection of the tonsils

tourniquet — tight band used to stop bleeding

trachea — tube connecting mouth and lungs; windpipe

trait — characteristic

tranquilizer — drug with a calming effect; can be emotionally habit-forming

tricep — muscle at the back of the upper arm

tumor — mass of tissue in lump form, caused by cells dividing abnormally and growing too rapidly

ulcer — open sore in the stomach or small intestine

ulna — upper arm bone

urethra — tube that takes urine out of the body; tube in the penis where sperm cells travel

urinary bladder — bag that stores urine

urine — liquid waste product formed in the kidneys

uterus — female body part that holds and nurtures a developing embryo; womb

vaccine — injected serum that causes the body to produce antibodies to a disease

vagina — reproductive organ of the female

value system — system of beliefs

valve — tissue that controls blood flow between parts of the heart

vein — blood vessel that carries waste products from cells back to the heart

venule — tiny vein

vertebrae — bones in the spinal column

villi — projections in the small intestine that absorb food

virus — disease-producing organism

vitamin — nutrient necessary for the body to function

voluntary muscle — muscle that a person can control

wax — coating that protects the ears

wellness — overall well-being; emotionally and physically healthy

white blood cell — disease-fighting part of the blood

wisdom tooth — very back molar

withdrawal symptom — pain, chills, fevor, or other bodily disorder caused by discontinuing the use of a drug, including alcohol

X chromosome — chromosome in the egg cell

Y chromosome — chromosome in the sperm cell

Index

Involuntary muscles   95

J

Jenner, Edward,   180
Joint   92, 93, 97, 99

K

Kidney failure   140–141
Kidney transplant   140-141
Kidneys   129, 139-141

L

Large intestine   129, 138, 141
Laxatives   131, 138
Lean body composition   159, 161, 173
Left atrium   69–70
Left ventricle   69, 70
Legally intoxicated   203
Leukemia   188
Life-style   3–5, 19, 22, 36
Ligaments   92–93, 99
Liver   66, 80, 127
Local emergency number   251
Love   223–224, 238
Lung cancer   137, 141, 210–211, 214
Lungs   123, 130–132, 135, 137, 141

M

Males   103–104, 113, 117
Malignant   186, 189
Malocclusion   164
Mammogram   187
Marijuana   195
Marriage   265, 269–270, 272–273, 276
Marrow   66, 67, 80, 87, 99
Maturity   27, 34–35, 37
Meat group   152, 173
Medulla   42, 59
Melanin   166
Meningitis   47, 59
Menstruation   111, 117
Mental well-being   3, 8, 9, 19
Microbes   178, 179–180, 189
Microorganisms   178
Migraine headache   46
Milk group   152, 173

Minerals   87, 146, 147, 151, 153, 173
Molars   163–164
Moles   170, 173
Morphine   196
Mothers Against Drunk Drivers
      (MADD)   206
Motorcycle   246, 260
Multiple sclerosis   47, 59
Muscle tone   96
Muscles   85, 95–97, 99
Muscular dystrophy   97, 99

N

Nearsightedness   53, 59
Negative behavior   229, 239
Nephrons   129
Nicotine   210, 212, 214
Noncommunicable diseases   182
Noncorrosive poison   257
Nostrils   122, 141
Nutrients   126, 128,–129, 131,
      145–146, 152, 173
Nutrition   145, 173

O

Ophthalmologist   54–55
Optic nerve   50, 59
Optometrist   54
Organisms   13
Organs   12, 13, 14
Osteoporosis   91, 150
Otosclerosis   56, 59
Ovarian cycle   111
Ovaries   27, 108, 117
Ovulation   107, 109, 111, 117

P

Pancreas   127
Pap smear   187
Paralysis   43, 47
Pathogens   177, 178, 181, 184, 189
Peer counselor   33
Peer pressure   33
Peers   206
Pelvis   88, 92
Penicillin   112–113